Stewardship

2nd Edition

Student Workbook

By Steven P. Demme

1-888-854-MATH (6284) — mathusee.com
sales@mathusee.com

Acknowledgments
Special thanks to the Stewardship team of graphic designers, videographers, content editors, and proofers who included: Jeff, Joseph, Isaac, Timothy, Heather, Dan, Miriam, Drew, Becca, Amy, Sherry, John, Beth, Renita, Bethany, and Catherine.

The students in the class, whose names you will see in some of the exercises, were: Maggie, Collin, Clayton, Abigail, Christianna, Darby, Adam, Faith, Rachel, Ernest, Isabella, Chloe, Madeline, Isaac, James, Teagan, Sarah, Anna, Savanah, Maddie , Cyrus, and Mercy. I am very grateful for these students for being my class as we filmed these sessions. They were a delight to teach, asking good questions, being attentive, finding mistakes, and for selecting my ties.

Ultimately all glory be to God for the great things He has accomplished through us.

Stewardship Student Workbook
2nd Edition

Published and distributed by Demme Learning

For support or other information: mathusee.com
1-888-854-6284 or +1 717-283-1448 | demmelearning.com
Lancaster, Pennsylvania USA

ISBN 978-1-60826-363-9
Revision Code Version 0619

For information regarding CPSIA on this printed material call: 1-888-854-6284
and provide reference #0619-061719

 To show reverence and be consistent, I have chosen to capitalize all pronouns which represent the Triune God in scripture references as well in my writing.

Contents

HOW TO TEACH STEWARDSHIP

Access the video instruction at stewardshipmath.com. Read through the Instruction Manual and the Biblical Studies book. Work through the Student Worksheets which have five worksheets per lesson. If you would like to have a test for each lesson consider setting aside one page for that purpose. When the problems have each been checked and compared with the Solutions in the back of the Instruction Manual, move on to the next lesson. There is a some continuity in this course, but each lesson can also studied as an independent unit.

SUPPORT AND RESOURCES

I will be adding resources to the lessons periodically. You will see in the books that there are links to podcasts and interviews with other knowledgeable people and recommended reading for more study.

A WORD ABOUT GRADING

We recognize that the instructor is the best judge of how well a student is progressing. Some instructors may choose not to issue grades at all, while others may be required to do so.

The Solutions give an answer for all student work and show how the student might arrive at a given solution. You will need to compare your student's answer to the sample to make sure the student understands the concept covered by the question. In cases where there is more than one way to solve a problem or more than one valid answer, the Solutions will only give one way of solving the problem and only one solution. Other solutions may be equally valid.

Stewardship contains many questions where students are expected to interview their parents or grandparents, apply their knowledge to their own unique situation, make lists of pros and cons, and answer open-ended questions about the Biblical Studies material. In all these cases, parents should discuss the student's answers with the student, but not assume that the solution given in the Solutions is the only correct answer. For example you may find a question which asks the student to compare three different items offered for sale and choose what they think is the best value. The Solutions will give my opinion on which is the best value, but if students think that one of the other options provides a better value it would be an excellent opportunity for parents to discuss the answer.

INVOLVEMENT OF THE FAMILY

Throughout the book, I will be asking the student to interview his or her parents for input on the lesson being studied. I do this for several reasons.

1. Parents have valuable experience and wisdom that their children need to hear. I am hoping that the questions in the lessons will facilitate discussion that will benefit parent and student alike. This curriculum is filled with stories and illustrations from Steve's life and understanding, but each parent and grandparent has their own wisdom and experience and I am hoping the student can learn from them.
2. Most of the lessons where these interview questions are found deal with topics that don't have a right or wrong answer. In discussing the topics you will see facets of the problem that you probably wouldn't have seen by yourself.
3. Parents have a God-given responsibility to teach and instruct their children. God tells us that His wisdom is to be passed on in everyday occurrences. "Repeat [God's commandments] again and again to your children. Talk about them

when you are at home and when you are on the road, when you are going to bed and when you are getting up" (Deuteronomy 6:7, NLT). These starter questions could be the topic of conversation around the dinner table or in the car.

GRANDPARENTS

There are also some questions for grandparents. While God's principles are eternal and applicable to all generations, they can be fleshed out differently in different time periods. When you discuss these topics with more seasoned people, notice trends from one generation to another. If you do not have ready access to your grandparents, perhaps a respected church member or elderly neighbor could help you complete your assignment.

As a father and a grandparent I have a lot of experiences and memories. It is my privilege to share many of them with you in the pages of this curriculum. But I hope you will also learn to patently listen to the experiences and wisdom of your grandparents as well as your parents. They have so much to offer. If you will humbly ask them to share what they have learned and draw them out by asking questions and being sincerely interested, you and these blessed seasoned citizens will have a wonderful experience.

Someday you will understand what it feels like to be a son, a father, and a grandfather at the same time. I will always be a son to my parents, and still feel like a young man at heart. I am also an older man with much to share with those who are teachable and willing to listen. Joel 2:28 makes an interesting observation of how the outpouring of the Spirit impacts sons, young men, and old men. "It shall come to pass afterward, that I will pour out my Spirit on all flesh; your sons and your daughters shall prophesy, your old men shall dream dreams, and your young men shall see visions."

As young adults you will have dreams, visions, and hopes for the future. That is right and is the way God has made you. The older people in your life also have drams, but they are mostly about the past. This is the way they are wired. Learn to appreciate each other's strengths and inclinations. Humble interaction between all ages in your family is what God designed when he made the wonderful institution of the family.

FOR THE STUDENT

I hope you have a healthy relationship with your parents and grandparents. God chose your family. He then gave instructions to parents and children. The one command that applies specifically to all of us is to honor our father and mother. Paul notes in Ephesians 6 that this is the only command accompanied with a promise. The promise is that you will live long and that it will go well with you. If our attitude toward our dad and mom is not what it should be, let's ask God to turn our heart toward our folks and their hearts toward us. Based on Malachi 4:6 and 1 John 5:14–15, I am confident He will do just what you ask. "He will turn the hearts of fathers to their children and the hearts of children to their fathers." (Malachi 4:6)

"This is the confidence that we have toward Him, that if we ask anything according to His will He hears us. And if we know that He hears us in whatever we ask, we know that we have the requests that we have asked of Him." (1 John 5:14–15)

Jesus Himself submitted to His parents. "And he went down with them and came to Nazareth and was submissive to them." (Luke 2:51)

I am pretty sure He was tempted to not honor them. When we are young we think we know a lot, but He really did! He was fully God and fully man. As a man, He was also successful in fighting the temptation to rebel and as such is uniquely qualified to help you and me do the same. "This High Priest of ours understands our weaknesses, for He faced all of the same testings we do, yet he did not sin." (Hebrews 4:15, NLT)

When you ask your parents for their input on the questions in the lessons, do so with a humble attitude and listen with a teachable spirit. God has placed you in your parents' home to learn from and to be discipled by them. Your attitude of honoring them will go a long way in determining whether this will be a positive experience for your family. You don't have to agree with all of their conclusions, but hear them out. They have your best interests at heart. The following verse in Hebrews was not specifically written for parents and children, but I think it does have application since your parents are your primary disciplers. Note the last phrase in particular. "Obey your leaders and submit to them, for they are keeping watch over your souls, as those who will have to give an account. Let them do this with joy and not with groaning, for that would be of no advantage to you." (Hebrews 13:17)

It is my prayer that as you work through this curriculum, "the God of our Lord Jesus Christ, the Father of glory, may give you the Spirit of wisdom and of revelation in the knowledge of Him." (Ephesians 1:17)

May God bless each of you as you work through these studies,

Steve Demme

Worksheet 1.1

Practice Questions

1. Clayton earns an hourly wage of $6.00 per hour and time-and-a-half for overtime. If he worked 34 hours, what are his wages for the first week?

   $ 204

2. During the second week, Clayton worked 43.5 hours. What are his wages for the second week including overtime pay?

   240
   31.5
   271.5

   $ 271.5

3. During the third week, Clayton worked 47 hours. What are his wages for the third week?

   240
   63
   303

   $303

4. Clayton is keeping a record of his wages and wants to know his average pay per hour (rounded to the nearest cent) for the first three weeks. Can you help him?

   $6.25

5. Abigail is being paid a weekly salary at $11.75 per hour. What can she expect her salary to be for 50 weeks if her contract is for 40 hours of life-guarding each week?

   $23,500

6. Abigail is paid a $27,000 salary per year. About how much money per hour does she make? (Assume 50 weeks of 40 hours each for a simplified estimate.)

   $13.5

7. Alex just sold his first house as a real estate salesman. His commission is 1.5%. The house sold for $179,500. How much money in commissions did Alex receive from the sale?

$2692.5

8. Christiana is being paid 11¢ for each DVD she places in a jacket with the paper insert. Last week she finished eight cases of 100 in six hours. How much money did she make altogether? What was her average pay per hour rounded to the nearest cent?

$88

$14.67 ph

Bible and Discussion Questions

9. Which one verse do you like the best about God owning everything?

Proverbs 3:9

10. How much of Scripture is inspired? How do we know?

11. Have your parents ever worked for a piecemeal wage? What kind of job was it?

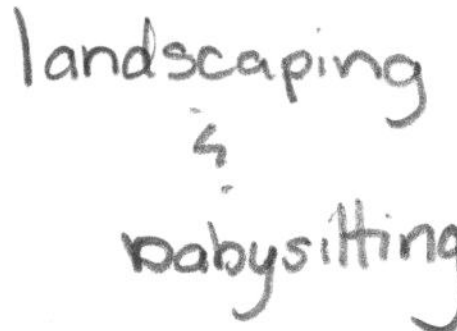

Worksheet 1.2

Practice Questions

1. James earns an hourly wage of $10.75 per hour and time-and-a-half for overtime. If he worked 38.5 hours, what are Joseph's wages (rounded to the nearest cent) for the first week he worked?

2. During the second week, James worked 51 hours. What are his wages for the second week rounded to the nearest cent?

3. During the third week, James worked 48.25 hours. What are his wages for the third week rounded to the nearest cent?

4. James is keeping a record of his pay. He wants to know his average pay per hour (rounded to the nearest cent) for the first three weeks. Can you help him?

5. John is being paid a weekly salary at $18.33 per hour and 40 hours per week. What can he expect his salary to be for 50 weeks?

6. Isaac is being paid a $44,500 salary per year. About how much money per hour does Isaac make? (Assume 50 weeks of 40-hours each for a simplified estimate.)

7. Anthony is a real estate salesman. He just sold a house to a customer. Because Anthony represented both the buyer and the seller, his commission is 1.5% for selling and another 1.5% for buying. The house closed for $112,000. How much money did he receive for his commission?

8. Dani makes 60¢ for filling a fraction kit with plastic inserts. She made 47 kits this week. How much was her check? How much was her hourly wage (rounded to the nearest cent) if she completed the work in 3 hours and 15 minutes?

BIBLE AND DISCUSSION QUESTIONS

9. What was God's appointed task for Adam and Eve in the garden of Eden?

10. What is the message of Deuteronomy 30:11 and 14?

11. What was your folk's first job that paid an hourly wage? How much were they paid?

Worksheet 1.3

Practice Questions

1. Story earns an hourly wage of $7.50 an hour. If she worked 25 hours, what is her pay for the week? During the second week, Story worked a total of 41 hours. What is her pay for the second week?

2. Anora receives a weekly salary for 40 hours per week at $8.25 per hour. Estimate her yearly income. (Use 50 weeks for the year to keep the estimate simple).

3. Cassie-Marie receives an annual salary of $52,500.00. About how much money per hour does she make? (Assume 50 weeks of 40-hours each to keep the estimate simple.)

4. Aimee just sold a set of encyclopedias for $950.00. Her commission is 15%. How much money did Aimee receive for this sale?

5. Maddie receives 45¢ for each set of inserts she assembles. She assembled 83 sets in 3 hours and 30 minutes. How much did money she earn? What was her hourly rate?

6. Would you rather receive a salary, be paid a commission for your work, or a combination of both? What are the advantages of each method of being recompensed for your efforts?

7. Debbie sells new cars. The price of an average new vehicle at her dealership is $23,000.00 and the profit for the dealership is $1,260.00 per car. Debbie receives a 25% commission on the dealership's profit for each car she sells. How much did she make when she sold seven cars in four weeks?

8. Debbie also receives a base salary of $450.00 each week. What is Debbie's total salary (base salary plus commissions) for the four weeks?

Bible and Discussion Questions

9. Define a steward in your own words.

10. Find two passages the teach that Jesus is the Word of God.

11. Did your mom or dad ever have a job where they were paid extra for working overtime?

Worksheet 1.4

Practice Questions

1. Jen is paid an hourly wage of $9.25 per hour. What are her wages for the week if she works 38 hours? The next week, Jen puts in 48 hours at work. How much do her wages come to for that week? Round your answer to the nearest cent.

2. Julia receives a weekly salary for 40 hours each week at $23.00 per hour. If she puts in 50 weeks, what is her salary?

3. According to her employment contract, Olivia will receive an annual salary of $75,000. Estimate the equivalent amount of money per hour. (Assume 50 weeks of 40 hours each to keep it simple.)

4. Anna found a buyer for a bread machine. The retail price is $375.00 and her commission is 24%. How much money did she make on the sale?

5. Lauren receives $1.25 for each block set she assembles. She assembled 28 sets in 2 hours and 45 minutes. How much money did she earn? What was her average pay per hour rounded to the nearest cent?

6. Would you rather be paid by the hour or by the piece? What are some advantages of each method of payment?

7. The studio offered Omar two options for his role as the lead actor in a movie. They would pay him a flat fee of $50,000.00 or a base pay of $10,000.00 plus 1% of the revenue generated from the sales from the first year. In his last feature film, the box office profit for the first year was $6,500,000.00. If this film is equally successful, which is the more lucrative option?

8. Omar does not need the money, so he made an offer to receive a commission of 1.5% of the revenue with no base fee. If the film generates a profit of $6,500,000.00, what will his commission be?

Bible and Discussion Questions

9. What is the primary qualification of a steward?

10. What are three benefits which follow reading God's word?

11. Which kind of pay do your parents prefer, hourly or piecemeal? Why?

Worksheet 2.1

Practice Questions

1. At the restaurant, Faith's bill came to $37.25. She left an 18% tip. How much money did the waiter receive if she computed the tip just on the food without the tax? The tax was 5% of the cost of the food. How much did the tax add to the bill?

2. Faith likes to pay in round numbers. What should she add to the tip in number 1 to make the final bill just dollars and no cents? What is the final tally?

3. This week Rachel and Ernest went to an "all-you-can-eat" spaghetti dinner. Ernest ate three plates of noodles and sauce. The bill was $26.95 for the two of them. How much is a 20% tip? The sales tax was 7%. How much did this add to their bill?

4. What was the final bill for the spaghetti dinner? Add a little extra for the server and round up to the nearest dollar.

5. Isaac received a bill on May 17 for $874.50. On the bottom of invoice is a line that reads "1% 10 net 30." It is now May 23. How much should he pay?

6. Isaac had an invoice come in for $1,358.00. On the bill it said "2% 15 net 30." It has been twenty-five days since he received the bill. Is he able to take advantage of the discount? If so, how much would he save?

Use this table for numbers 7-8

Property Tax	$2,573.92
If paid in April or May	5% discount
If paid in June or July	2% discount
If paid in August or September	No adjustment
If paid after September 30	1% penalty

7. If the property tax bill is paid in April, how much will it be?

8. What is the total amount if the payment is sent in on October 29?

Bible and Discussion Questions

9. What is the first and great commandment?

10. What specific chapters in the Bible are topical studies?

11. What month(s) do your parents pay their large recurring bills, such as property tax?

Worksheet 2.2

Practice Questions

1. Savannah was eating at the Outfront Steak House. The bill came to $76.85. She left a 16% tip, computing the tip on just the food without the tax. How much did the server receive? The sales tax was 6.75%. How much did this add to her bill?

2. Savannah prefers to pay in even dollars. How much did she add to the bill to round up to the nearest dollar?

3. For Anna's birthday, she went to Carrumbbas Restaurant. The bill was $93.20. How much would a 15% tip come to? The sales tax was 7.25%. How much did this add to the bill?

4. What is the final tally for the meal at Carrumbbas, including the tax and tip? Round the answer to the nearest dollar.

5. A bill was received on August 9 for $1,299.00. On the invoice is a note that said "1% 10 net 30." It is now August 20th. How much should be sent?

6. An invoice came for $265.00. On the bill it said "2% 10 net 30." It has been seven days since this was received this in the mail. How much should be paid if the payment is sent in today?

Use this table for numbers 7-8

Property Tax	$1,802.73
If paid in April or May	5% discount
If paid in June or July	2% discount
If paid in August or September	No adjustment
If paid after September 30	1% penalty

7. If I pay my property tax bill in July, how much will it be?

8. What is the total amount if I send my payment in on September 19?

Bible and Discussion Questions

9. According to Jesus in Luke 16:13, is it possible to serve two masters? Why not?

10. What are some passages that speak to having our minds transformed by studying the truth?

11. What are some of the incentives that tipping brings to the marketplace?

Worksheet 2.3

Practice Questions

1. The bill at Ruby Mondays came to $29.60. I left a 16% tip. How much money does the faithful waiter receive if the tip is computed on just the food portion? The sales tax was 6%. How much did this add to the bill?

2. What was the total bill rounded down to the nearest dollar?

3. Your dad received a bill on August 1 for $1,075.00. On the invoice is a note that says "2% 10 net 30." It is now August 12. How much should he send?

4. If he had paid it on August 8th, how much could he have saved? How much would he have paid with the discount deducted?

5. Catherine is a generous tipper and pays $2.00 per bag for help in parking shuttles and at curbside check-in. She has three bags on this trip. How much did she spend in total tips?

6. What does "2% 15 Net 30 days" mean?

Use this table for numbers 7-8

Property Tax	$3,573.92
If paid in April or May	5% discount
If paid in June or July	2% discount
If paid in August or September	No adjustment
If paid after September 30	1% penalty

7. How much do I save by paying in May?

8. How much extra do I pay if I wait until October to pay the bill?

Bible and Discussion Questions

9. How would you define an idol? What are some examples of things which could easily become an idol to you?

10. What did you think as you read the list of verses about the goodness of God?

11. Can you think of any other occupations, in addition to food servers, where tips are involved?

Worksheet 2.4

Practice Questions

1. My wife was gone most of the day. When she returned home, we looked for a Chinese buffet for our dinner. There were four of us, and the charge was $9.50 per person. How much would the cost of the food be for all of us?

2. The sales tax was 6.5%. Since it was a buffet, we left only a 5% tip. What was our total tab?

3. Chloe, Madeline, and Isabella Peters went to a swanky eating place. Their combined bill came to $147.50. The sales tax in that state is 7%. How much did the tax add to the bill?

4. These ladies received excellent service throughout the meal and decided to leave an 18% tip. How much was the tip?

5. The Peters sisters divvied up the bill three ways. How much did they each pay?

6. An invoice arrived for $2,857.00. In small print it reads "2% 15 net 30." How much will I save by paying 10 days after I receive the invoice?

Use this table for numbers 7-8

Property Tax	$1,902.73
If paid in April or May	5% discount
If paid in June or July	2% discount
If paid in August or September	No adjustment
If paid after September 30	1% penalty

7. How much do I save by paying in June?

8. How much will I pay if I send in the check on August 31?

Bible and Discussion Questions

9. How can money be an idol?

10. What are some benefits that Steve has found in studying Bible topics?

11. Where do your parents leave tips?

Worksheet 3.1

Practice Questions

1. What is your gross weekly paycheck if you earn $22,800.00 annually and receive 52 paychecks per year? What are your tax withholdings for each check? The Federal Withholding is calculated for you.

Gross Weekly Pay	______
Federal Withholding	$40.00
State	______
County	______
FICA	______
SUI	______
Total	______

2. What tax is the highest for you?

3. What tax is the lowest for you?

4. What is your weekly take home pay?

5. If you choose to write a tithe check on your gross pay, how much will you return to God?

6. How much does your employer contribute?

Gross Weekly Pay	________
FUTA	________
FICA	________
SUI	________
Total	________

7. What percent of your gross pay is your take home pay?

Bible and Discussion Questions

8. What is love and how does God show His love to us?

9. Who created and designed the family? What are the parents' responsibility within the institution of the family?

10. Do your parents and/or grandparents calculate their own taxes, or do they have an accountant prepare them? If they do hire an accountant, how did they choose the one they have? How much does he charge?

Worksheet 3.2

Practice Questions

1. Last year you were a real estate salesman earning only your commission with no base salary. You sold an average of one house per week, and the average price of each house was $78,000.00. What was the total amount of your sales for the year (52 weeks)?

2. If your commission was 1.5%, estimate your gross income and your average weekly gross income.

3. Compute the amount of taxes which are deducted from your average weekly income.

Gross Weekly Pay	________
Federal Withholding	$0.00
State	________
County	________
FICA	________
SUI	________
Total	________

4. What is your weekly take home pay?

5. If you contribute 10% of your weekly take-home pay, what is your weekly contribution?

6. Before studying this unit on taxes, how much of your paycheck did you estimate would be taken out for taxes?

7. What percent could you multiply by your gross pay in order to estimate your take home pay without subtracting each individual tax?

Bible and Discussion Questions

8. What is the essence of coveting? Where do we read about not coveting?

9. What does it mean to honor someone?

10. Ask your parents what the percentages for the state and local taxes are where you live.

Worksheet 3.3

Practice Questions

1. As a self-employed assembler, Victoria assembled 1,485 cases of DVDs at her home. She was reimbursed 11¢ per DVD, and there were 100 DVDs in a case. What was her gross income for assembling these?

2. What will her taxable income be after she has deducted the standard deduction of $12,000.00 for a single person?

3. How much does she estimate her quarterly payments for FICA will be?

4. When does she have to pay the quarterly payments?

5. At the end of the year, she will begin making plans to file her taxes. How much should she set aside for federal taxes?

6. How much will she owe in state and local taxes if the rates are 3.07% and 1%?

7. Since her income is irregular, meaning some months she earns more than other months, how should she tithe?

Bible and Discussion Questions

8. In your own words, what is the difference between loving and coveting?

9. Does God's word ask us to honor our parents only if they are honorable? Are there any perfect parents or perfect children spoken of in scripture besides God the Father and Jesus the Son?

10. Are your parents self-employed or do they work for an employer? Have they ever been self-employed? If they were self-employed, who assisted them with their taxes?

Worksheet 3.4

Practice Questions

1. John wants to be a math teacher like his father. He graduates from college and his first teaching assignment is in Pennsylvania, where the average annual starting salary is $54,000.00. Before we begin computing the actual taxes, let's estimate based on what we have already observed. Approximately how much will his annual take home salary be?

2. Estimate his FICA, state, and local taxes.

3. Approximately how much will John earn weekly?

4. How much will be withheld from his paycheck for taxes?

Gross Weekly Pay	____________
Federal Withholding	$132.00
State	____________
County	____________
FICA	____________
SUI	____________
Total	____________

5. How much will his employer contribute?

Gross Weekly Pay	____________
FUTA	____________
FICA	____________
SUI	____________
Total	____________

6. How much will he be able to tithe on his gross pay each month?

7. What does FICA mean and what are the two components and their percentages that comprise the FICA tax?

Bible and Discussion Questions

8. The whole law and the prophets are based on two commandments. What are they?

9. What is the first commandment with a promise and where is it found in the Bible?

10. Ask your parents about some advantages of hiring an accountant.

Worksheet 4.1

Practice Questions

1. Name two functions of a bank.

2. Whose money is in a bank?

3. Tell one way that a bank makes money.

4. If you withdraw $300.00 from an ATM and pay a fee of $1.50, what percentage of the amount withdrawn is the fee?

5. The bill for the lunch was $36.00. The tax was 8.5% and the tip was 16%. Can you employ the short cut for percents to make one calculation to determine the final charge for the meal? (Hint: add once and multiply once.)

6. How do you qualify for free checking?

7. You and three of your friends have formed a landscaping company called "You Sow, We Mow." Your clientele consists of five of your neighbors and the business generates $290.00 per week. If you are each receiving 25% of the profit, how much do you each make in one week?

Bible and Discussion Questions

8. What does this passage mean? "Godliness with contentment is great gain."

9. How was Steve's prayer to love God with everything in him answered?

10. Where do your parents do their banking? Why did they choose this particular bank?

Worksheet 4.2

Practice Questions

1. Why do you have to pay fees on a checking account if you keep only a few dollars in your account and write several checks per month?

2. What is a passbook?

3. What is home equity?

4. Why do you need to be able to access an ATM machine?

5. The bill for dinner was $88.00. The tax was 6% and the tip was 15%. Can you employ the shortcut for percents and make one calculation to determine the final charge for the meal? (Hint: add once and multiply once.)

6. What is the fee for withdrawing money from your home bank's ATM machine?

7. You Sow, We Mow just gained two new customers but lost one of the partners. The three of you are now mowing seven yards and have a gross profit of $400.00 per week. How much did you each earn for two weeks work?

Bible and Discussion Questions

8. What is the Biblical antidote for coveting?

9. In 2012, God quickened a passage of scripture to make Steve know: “As much as God the Father loves Jesus the Son, in the exact same way, Jesus loves me.” What is that verse?

10. Which services at the bank do your parents use?

Worksheet 4.3

Practice Questions

1. Which is the safest place to save money, a shoebox or a bank?

2. What is a savings account?

3. What is a deposit?

4. I was shopping at Kohl's this weekend and discovered they had a 40% discount on every item purchased. How much did I spend on three shirts which originally cost $45.00 each? How much did I save?

5. Can you do #4 by multiplying once instead of multiplying then subtracting? Does your answer agree with #4?

6. George and Johnny were looking for work and had some experience with exterior painting. They began a new company called "Don't Faint, We Paint." Since Johnny owned the ladders and they would be using his truck, he was to receive 60% of the profit, and George would be paid 40%. The first two jobs netted a profit of $2,400.00. How much did they each make?

7. Johnny and George ate lunch at the McDonough Diner. Their bill came to $24.80 for the food plus a 5% tax and a 20% tip. How much was the total bill? They each paid half. What were their individual bills?

Bible and Discussion Questions

8. What is the message of the hymn "Count Your Blessings?"

9. What has Steve learned about the connection between his vertical relationship with God and his horizontal relationships with his wife, family, and neighbors?

10. Ask your folks to arrange the following features in order of importance to them: customer service, convenience (location), interest rates, and fees.

Worksheet 4.4

Practice Questions

1. What words are associated with banks to engender your confidence?

2. What is the difference between a lender and a borrower?

3. What does ATM represent?

4. What word describes a long-term loan for a home?

5. I set out to buy a new chair which cost $288, but was on sale for 20% off. What is the easiest way to find out how much the chair will cost after the discount?

6. The second year of "Don't Faint, We Paint," Johnny and George were able to hire two more employees, Brad and Nate. They decided on the following percentages for the crew: Johnny 40%, George 30%, Brad 15%, Nate 15%. That month the business prospered, and they had a net profit of $16,500.00. What did each person make?

7. "Don't Faint, We Paint" is based in North Carolina, where they have a flat state income tax of 5.8%. If we compute the federal tax as 12% and the local taxes as 1.2%, how much will Johnny's take-home pay be from #6?

Bible and Discussion Questions

8. What is the command in Hebrews 13:5?

9. There are nine scriptures listed under "We are Children of God." Which one(s) touched your heart?

10. Where do your grandparents do their banking? Why did they choose this particular bank?

Worksheet 4.5

Practice Questions

1. What are the responsibilities of a loan officer at a bank?

2. What is it called if you do not make your loan payments on time?

3. What is a repossession?

4. If you ever secure a loan from a bank, you will need collateral. What is collateral?

5. Which kind of account generally pays a better interest percentage, a savings account or a checking account?

6. Part way through the second year of "Don't Faint, We Paint," Johnny and George sat down to reevaluate the percentages, since Brad and Nate were working so well. They made the following changes: Johnny 34%, George 28%, Brad 19%, Nate 19%. The following month the business had a gross profit of $21,975.00. It also had expenses of $3,400. What was the take home pay for each member of the team?

7. If the flat state income tax is 5.8%, and we compute the federal tax as 9% and the local taxes as 1.7%, how much will George's take home pay be from #6?

Bible and Discussion Questions

8. What is the promise in Hebrews 13:5?

9. Meditate on Ephesians 1:4-5, and then restate the truths in this passage in your own words.

10. Ask your grandparents to arrange the following features in order of importance to them: customer service, convenience (location), interest rates, and fees.

Worksheet 5.1

Practice Questions

Joe and Josephine Unit
369 Decimal Street
Place Value, PA 17606

NEIGHBOR'S BANK
12 Main Street
Goodtown, PA 17601
60-1234/0313

1556

DATE *May 19, 2019*

PAY TO THE ORDER OF *Manny Tens* $ *125.00*

One hundred twenty-five and 00/100 DOLLARS

MEMO *downpayment boat*

Joseph B. Unit
AUTHORIZED SIGNATURE

⑆031312343⑆1556 0898765402⑈

1. Who is writing the check and authorizing the payment?

2. Who is the check made out to, or who receives the money?

3. What is the amount and where is it recorded?

4. What is the number of the check?

5. You are Joe or Josephine Unit. Write out a check to Jack Taylor for $279.00. This is for partial payment for a guitar. Make sure to sign your name and date the check with today's date.

Joe and Josephine Unit
369 Decimal Street
Place Value, PA 17606

NEIGHBOR'S BANK
12 Main Street
Goodtown, PA 17601
60-1234/0313

1557

DATE ____________

PAY TO THE ORDER OF ______________________________ $[ ]

______________________________ DOLLARS

MEMO ____________________ ____________________
AUTHORIZED SIGNATURE

⑆031312343⑆1557 0898765402⑈

6. After receiving a check from a friend for $100, you decide to give it to your dad to help with your car insurance payment which he has already paid. On the back of the first check, sign it and endorse it to your dad using his name.

First Check

ENDORSE HERE

DO NOT WRITE, SIGN, OR STAMP BELOW THIS LINE

Reserved for Financial Institution use

Second Check

ENDORSE HERE

DO NOT WRITE, SIGN, OR STAMP BELOW THIS LINE

Reserved for Financial Institution use

7. Endorse the back of the second check for a deposit.

8. It is the time of the month to reconcile your checking account. First enter which checks and deposits have cleared. Then compare your balance with the balance on your statement.

ACCOUNT STATEMENT

Statement Date	06-18-2019
Beginning Date	05-19-2019
Previous Balance	$305.40

Date	Transaction	Deposits/Credits	Payments/Debits	Balance	Checks Paid #	Checks Paid Date	Checks Paid Amount
5/23	Check 475		25.00	280.40	475	5/23	25.00
5/28	Check 476		15.00	265.40	476	5/28	15.00
5/27	Deposit	360.00		625.40	477	6/01	50.00
6/01	Check 477		50.00	575.40	480	6/18	25.00
6/18	Check 480		25.00	550.40			

■AD-Automatic Deposit ■AP-Automatic Payment ■ATM-Teller Machine ■DC-Debit Card ■T-Tax Deductible ■TT-Telephone Transfer

NUMBER OR CODE	DATE	TRANSACTION DESCRIPTION	PAYMENT AMOUNT		☑	FEE	DEPOSIT AMOUNT		BALANCE	
									305	40
475	5/20	Guitar lesson	25	00					280	40
476	5/25	Swimming class	15	00					265	40
	5/27	Deposited paycheck					360	00	625	40
477	5/27	Focus on the Family	50	00					575	40
478	6/13	Car insurance	60	00					515	65
479	6/15	Cell phone	34	75					480	65
480	6/18	Cash	25	00					455	65

9. Reconcile your bank statement.

BALANCE THIS STATEMENT		550	40
Add			
Deposits made since this statement			
SUBTOTAL			
Checks issued but not on the statement			
Number	Amount		
TOTAL OUTSTANDING CHECKS			
Subtract (total outstanding checks from subtotal)			
CURRENT BALANCE			

BIBLE AND DISCUSSION QUESTIONS

10. How is our heart connected to our treasure?

11. Which two verses encourage Steve each morning when he first awakes?

12. How do your folks reconcile their checking account? Do they access their account online?

Worksheet 5.2

Practice Questions

Joe and Josephine Unit
369 Decimal Street
Place Value, PA 17606

NEIGHBOR'S BANK
12 Main Street
Goodtown, PA 17601
60-1234/0313

1556

DATE *May 19, 2019*

PAY TO THE ORDER OF *Manny Tens* $ *125.00*

One hundred twenty-five and 00/100 DOLLARS

MEMO *downpayment boat*

Joseph B. Unit
AUTHORIZED SIGNATURE

⑆031312343⑆1556 0898765402⑈

1. What is the bank routing number?

2. What two places have the routing number?

3. What is the address of the bank?

4. What is the function of the memo line?

5. You are Joe Unit, or Josephine, as the case may be. Write out a check to Ricky Ricardo for $1,595.84. This is for a set of bongo drums. Make sure to sign your name and date the check with today's date.

Joe and Josephine Unit
369 Decimal Street
Place Value, PA 17606

NEIGHBOR'S BANK
12 Main Street
Goodtown, PA 17601
60-1234/0313

1558

DATE ____________

PAY TO THE ORDER OF ______________________________ $[ ]

______________________________ DOLLARS

MEMO ______________________ ______________________
AUTHORIZED SIGNATURE

⑆031312343⑆1558 0898765402⑈

6. After receiving a check from a friend for $50.00, you decide to give it to your brother (or sister). On the back of the first check, sign it and endorse it to your sibling using his or her name.

First Check

ENDORSE HERE

DO NOT WRITE, SIGN, OR STAMP BELOW THIS LINE

Reserved for Financial Institution use

Second Check

ENDORSE HERE

DO NOT WRITE, SIGN, OR STAMP BELOW THIS LINE

Reserved for Financial Institution use

7. Endorse the back of the second check to be cashed.

8. It is the time of the month to reconcile your checking account. First enter which checks and deposits have cleared. Then compare your balance with the balance on your statement.

Account Statement

Statement Date 07-18-2019
Beginning Date 06-19-2019
Previous Balance $455.65

Date	Transaction	Deposits/Credits	Payments/Debits	Balance
6/22	Check 481		69.96	385.69
6/30	Check 482		102.50	283.19
6/27	Deposit	360.00		643.19
7/14	Check 484		4.20	638.99

Checks Paid		
#	Date	Amount
481	6/22	69.96
482	6/27	102.50
484	7/14	4.20

▪AD-Automatic Deposit ▪AP-Automatic Payment ▪ATM-Teller Machine ▪DC-Debit Card ▪T-Tax Deductible ▪TT-Telephone Transfer

NUMBER OR CODE	DATE	TRANSACTION DESCRIPTION	PAYMENT AMOUNT	☑	FEE	DEPOSIT AMOUNT	BALANCE
							455.65
481	6/20	Barnes and Noble	69.96				385.19
482	6/25	Radio Shack	102.50				283.19
	6/27	Deposited paycheck				360.00	643.19
483	6/27	Calvary Church	36.00				607.19
484	7/13	Library fees	4.20				602.99
485	7/15	Video rental	8.55				594.44
	7/19	Deposited tax refund				178.21	772.65

Reconcile your bank statement.

BALANCE THIS STATEMENT		638.99
Add		
Deposits made since this statement		
SUBTOTAL		
Checks issued but not on the statement		
Number	Amount	
TOTAL OUTSTANDING CHECKS		
Subtract (total outstanding checks from subtotal)		
CURRENT BALANCE		

Bible and Discussion Questions

9. As you read through the studies about the heart, which one scripture stood out to you? And what is meaningful?

10. What does it mean to be unconditionally loved by our Heavenly Father?

11. Where do your parents use checks? Do they use them to buy groceries, pay a mechanic, or pay bills through the mail?

Worksheet 5.3

Practice Questions

1. It is the time of the month to reconcile your checking account. First enter which checks and deposits have cleared.

Account Statement

Statement Date	03-01-2018
Beginning Date	03-31-2018
Previous Balance	$264.70

Date	Transaction	Deposits/Credits	Payments/Debits	Balance	Checks Paid #	Checks Paid Date	Checks Paid Amount
3/11	Deposit	240.00		504.70			
3/16	Check 203		45.00	459.70	203	3/16	45.00
3/17	Check 205		100.00	359.70	205	3/17	100.00
3/28	Check 206		32.45	327.25	206	3/28	32.45

■AD-Automatic Deposit ■AP-Automatic Payment ■ATM-Teller Machine ■DC-Debit Card ■T-Tax Deductible ■TT-Telephone Transfer

NUMBER OR CODE	DATE	TRANSACTION DESCRIPTION	PAYMENT AMOUNT		☑	FEE	DEPOSIT AMOUNT		BALANCE	
									264	70
203	3/07	Computer software	45	00					219	70
204	3/10	Singing lessons	75	00					144	70
	3/10	Deposited bday check					240	00	384	70
205	3/12	Joni and Friends	100	00					284	70
206	3/19	Flowers for Morris bday	32	45					252	25
207	3/27	Cash	50	00					202	25
	3/31	Deposited tax refund					125	76	328	01

Now compare your balance with the balance on your statement. Does it agree? Why or why not?

2. Add all checks and deposits that have not cleared and add them to the balance then reconcile your statement. Does it agree now?

BALANCE THIS STATEMENT		327	25
Add Deposits made since this statement			
SUBTOTAL			
Checks issued but not on the statement			
Number	Amount		
TOTAL OUTSTANDING CHECKS			
Subtract (total outstanding checks from subtotal)			
CURRENT BALANCE			

3. What does a check statement tell you?

4. What is an overdraft?

5. What is a foreign ATM?

6. How do you avoid ATM fees?

Bible and Discussion Questions

7. What does scripture mean when it speaks of our heart?

8. In your own words, what does John 15:9 mean?

9. Approximately how many checks do your parents use each month?

Worksheet 5.4

Practice Questions

1. It is the time of the month to reconcile your checking account. First enter which checks and deposits have cleared.

Account Statement

Statement Date 08-01-2018
Beginning Date 08-31-2018
Previous Balance $441.25

Date	Transaction	Deposits/Credits	Payments/Debits	Balance	Checks Paid #	Checks Paid Date	Checks Paid Amount
8/09	Deposit	475.00		916.25			
8/10	Check 356		17.50	898.75	356	8/10	17.50
8/10	Check 357		53.95	844.80	357	8/10	53.95
8/19	Check 358		47.50	797.30	358	8/19	47.50

▪AD-Automatic Deposit ▪AP-Automatic Payment ▪ATM-Teller Machine ▪DC-Debit Card ▪T-Tax Deductible ▪TT-Telephone Transfer

Number or Code	Date	Transaction Description	Payment Amount		☑	Fee	Deposit Amount		Balance	
									441	25
356	8/01	Strasburg mini-golf	17	50					423	75
357	8/05	Circuit city	53	95					369	80
	8/08	Deposited paycheck					475	00	844	80
358	8/10	1st Community Church	47	50					797	30
359	8/24	Goodwill	18	70					778	60
360	8/25	Wawa gas station	40	00					738	60

2. Now compare your balance with the balance on your statement. Does it agree? Why or why not?

3. Add any deposits that have not cleared and add them to the balance.

BALANCE THIS STATEMENT		797	30
Add Deposits made since this statement			
SUBTOTAL			
Checks issued but not on the statement			
Number	Amount		
TOTAL OUTSTANDING CHECKS			
Subtract (total outstanding checks from subtotal)			
CURRENT BALANCE			

4. How does an ATM fee or insufficient funds charge appear on your monthly statement?

5. How does interest appear on your statement?

6. What is a credit union and why are they worth considering for your banking needs?

7. What is the difference between a bank and a credit union?

Bible and Discussion Questions

8. Why is our heart so important to us?

9. Which verse gives us insight about how God's love is poured into our hearts? Write it out please.

10. Where do your grandparents use checks? To buy groceries, pay a mechanic, or pay bills through the mail? Approximately how many checks do they use each month?

Worksheet 6.1

Practice Questions

1. What is income? What are some sources of income?

2. What is the difference between a want and a need? What are examples of needs?

3. Name at least three possible uses of a surplus.

4. Are you an enveloper? What is that exactly?

5. Using the chart at the end of Lesson 6 in the instruction manual, figure out the approximate amount of money for each category based on an annual salary of $25,000.00

Gross Income	$25,000.00
Tithe	________
Taxes	________
Net Spendable	________
Housing	________
Food	________
Auto	________
Insurance	________
Debts	________
Recreation	________
Clothing	________
Savings	________
Medical/Dental	________
Miscellaneous	________

6. Now that you have some guidelines from #5, here are actual numbers for those same categories over the course of a year. Which figures are a cause for concern, and why?

Gross Income	$25,000.00
Tithe	$2,500.00
Taxes	$3,750.00
Net Spendable	$18,125.00
Housing	$7,144.00
Food	$2,286.00
Auto	$2,643.00
Insurance	$880.00
Debts	$1,200.00
Recreation	$1,400.00
Clothing	$895.00
Savings	$350.00
Medical/Dental	$410.00
Miscellaneous	$917.00

7. What is the suggested limit for housing, food, and auto expenses?

BIBLE AND DISCUSSION QUESTIONS

8. Why is Steve concerned about debt?

9. Why is Jesus called our Savior? What did he come to save us from?

10. Do your parents have a budget? If not, do they see the value in having one? If they do, ask them to explain how they budget.

Worksheet 6.2

Practice Questions

1. What is out-go, and what are some examples in your experience?

2. What is the value of documenting where your money is spent?

3. Major question: Why have a budget?

4. Is there one budget plan that fits everyone? Please expound on that answer.

5. Using the chart at the end of Lesson 6 in the instruction manual, figure out the approximate amount of money for each category based on an annual salary of $40,000.00.

Gross Income	$40,000.00
Tithe	
Taxes	
Net Spendable	
Housing	
Food	
Auto	
Insurance	
Debts	
Recreation	
Clothing	
Savings	
Medical/Dental	
Miscellaneous	
Investments	

6. Now that you have some guidelines from #5, here are actual numbers for those same categories over the course of a year. Which figures are a cause for concern, and why?

Gross Income	$40,000.00
Tithe	$4,000.00
Taxes	$7,200.00
Net Spendable	$28,800.00
Housing	$8,640.00
Food	$3,380.00
Auto	$4,134.00
Insurance	$1,437.00
Debts	$1,250.00
Recreation	$2,009.00
Clothing	$1,975.00
Savings	$1,440.00
Medical/Dental	$1,044.00
Miscellaneous	$1,241.00
Investments	$2,250.00

7. Why is it a helpful idea to keep a record of how much you spend?

BIBLE AND DISCUSSION QUESTIONS

8. Is it sinful to borrow money?

9. Why are believers in Jesus well-pleasing to the Father?

10. What are some recurring expenses for your mom and dad? What are their largest annual expenditures?

Worksheet 6.3

Practice Questions

1. Keep a record of all the money you spend for two weeks. Create at least four budget categories for your expenditures.

2. Why is the information gleaned from a record of what you actually spend valuable?

3. Using the chart at the end of Lesson 6 in the instruction manual, figure out the approximate amount of money for each category based on an annual salary of $15,000.00.

Gross Income	$15,000.00
Tithe	________
Taxes	________
Net Spendable	________
Housing	________
Food	________
Auto	________
Insurance	________
Debts	________
Recreation	________
Clothing	________
Savings	________
Medical/Dental	________
Misc.	________

4. Now that you have some guidelines from #5, here are actual numbers for those same categories over the course of a year. Which figures are a cause for concern, and why?

Gross Income	$15,000.00
Tithe	$1,500.00
Taxes	$1,200.00
Net Spendable	$12,300.00
Housing	$4,305.00
Food	$1,850.00
Auto	$2,000.00
Insurance	$600.00
Debts	$845.00
Recreation	$550.00
Clothing	$1,115.00
Savings	$200.00
Medical/Dental	$425.00
Misc.	$395.00

5. In a nutshell, Steve believes in spending less than he earns. What do you think of that philosophy?

6. How much income do you have each month? How much do you save each month?

7. What recurring monthly expenses do you have?

Bible and Discussion Questions

8. What is one result of sin mentioned in Isaiah 59?

9. What should we say when asked about our plans for the future?

10. Ask your parents what advice they have about going into debt.

Worksheet 6.4

Practice Questions

1. Looking at your personal record of spending, what surprised you the most?

2. What was your largest expenditure? If you continue to spend this much money for an entire year, how much moola will have passed through your hands?

3. Using the chart at the end of Lesson 6 in the instruction manual, figure out the approximate amount of money for each category based on an annual salary of $50,000.00. Use the same percentages given on the chart for $40,000.

Gross Income	$50,000.00
Tithe	______
Taxes	______
Net Spendable	______
Housing	______
Food	______
Auto	______
Insurance	______
Debts	______
Recreation	______
Clothing	______
Savings	______
Medical/Dental	______
Misc.	______
Investments	______

4. Now that you have some guidelines from #5, here are actual numbers for those same categories over the course of a year. Which figures are a cause for concern, and why?

Gross Income	$50,000.00
Tithe	$5,000.00
Taxes	$9,000.00
Net Spendable	$36,000.00
Housing	$11,000.00
Food	$4,150.00
Auto	$4,975.00
Insurance	$1,750.00
Debts	$1,900.00
Recreation	$2,700.00
Clothing	$2,400.00
Savings	$2,100.00
Medical/Dental	$1,275.00
Misc.	$2,300.00
Investments	$2,550.00

5. Steve spends money with checks, credit cards, and cash. How do you conduct commerce?

6. How much time do you think you spend each day: sleeping, eating, studying, reading, on social media, etc.?

7. Keep track of how much time you spend at each task for one day, since your time is a significant part of your treasure.

Bible and Discussion Questions

8. What does it mean to presume?

9. How many sins do you have after asking Jesus to forgive them?

10. How do your grandparents budget? What lessons have they learned from their experiences when budgeting or not budgeting?

Worksheet 7.1

Practice Questions

1. What is a retail price? Who pays retail prices?

2. What does a retailer do for you?

3. Name a few of the costs or expenses a retailer has in the course of running his business and providing this service to you.

4. What is the average markup for a retailer? Give the answer as a percentage of the retail price of an item.

5. What is an average markup for a grocer? Write this as a percentage of the retail price.

6. If the shoes cost $35.00 wholesale and $59.00 retail, what is the markup in dollars?

7. The markup in #6 is what percent of the retail? What percent of the wholesale price is the markup? Give the answer to the nearest percent.

Bible and Discussion Questions

8. Who gives the power to acquire wealth? How do you know this is true?

9. Explain 2 Corinthians 5:21 in your own words.

10. Share with your family why John Wanamaker promoted price tags. What do they think of that information?

Worksheet 7.2

Practice Questions

1. What does wholesale mean?

2. What services does a wholesaler provide to you, the consumer, and to a retail outlet?

3. What are some of the expenses the wholesaler incurs?

4. Ethan bought a book about Alaska last week. It cost $16.00. The wholesale price is $9.00. What percent of the retail is the wholesale price?

5. In #4, what percent of the wholesale is the markup? Round to the nearest percent.

6. The price of a gallon of milk at Kroger is $2.89. If the wholesale price is 12% off of the retail price, what is the wholesale price?

7. Kroger sold 2,400 gallons of milk on Monday. What was their profit?

BIBLE AND DISCUSSION QUESTIONS

8. If you are not wealthy, does this mean God does not love you as much as those who are rich? Give an example of someone in Scripture who was not rich but blessed.

9. Steve is hoping for white clothes someday. Where in the Bible are people who also have white garments?

10. Where is your family's favorite place to buy discounted products or services?

Worksheet 7.3

Practice Questions

1. Maplehofe Dairy sells lemonade for 85¢ a pint. It costs them 25¢ to produce it. What is their profit? What percent of the retail is the profit?

2. Maplehofe also sells Polly Purebred Purified Water for 89¢ a pint. They don't produce it but must buy it from a middleman for 69¢ per bottle. What is their profit? What percent of the retail is the profit?

3. Which of the items do you think they will encourage their customers to purchase, the lemonade or the water? Why?

4. Which item are they most likely to discount? Why?

5. Joseph bought a DVD for $14.99. The wholesale price is 65% of the retail price. What is the wholesale price?

6. Stephanie is selling flowers. She can buy them at the wholesale price of $5.00 per bunch. What price should she sell them for if the wholesale price is 40% of the retail price?

7. The manager of the corner store was trying to decide which of the many items he sells provides the most profit. He found he sold 120 gallons of bottled water each week. He buys them for $1.25 a gallon and sells them for $1.79 a gallon. His next best-selling item is cheese, which he buys for $1.83 per pound and retails it for $2.99 a pound. If he sold 40 pounds of cheese each week, which item would provide more gross profit, the water or the cheese?

BIBLE AND DISCUSSION QUESTIONS

8. What are some of the possible dangers of wealth?

9. Who received new clothes in the book of Zechariah? Where else does a prophet speak of a robe of righteousness?

10. Where was the last place your family has seen a sale described as a percentage discount?

Worksheet 7.4

Practice Questions

1. Anna wrote a book on how to teach music to your children. She printed 500 of them for $1,700.00. How much is the cost of each book?

2. Her husband is marketing and selling Anna's books to bookstores for $7.50. The bookstores in turn are asking $14.99 for each book. For each book sold to the bookstore, Anna and her husband are making a profit of ________. Every time a happy customer buys one of Anna's books at the store, the bookstore makes a profit of ________.

3. How many books does Anna need to sell to bookstores to recover her initial investment in printing the books?

4. If Anna sells the books herself at book fairs and online for $14.99 each, how many will she need to sell to make $1,700.00? What percent of the retail is her profit if she sells them from home? Find the answer to the nearest percent.

5. Vicki sold 28 sets of encyclopedias last quarter. Her commission check was $3,500.00. How much did she make on each set? The cost of a set is $595.00. What percent of the retail was her commission?

6. Mr. Evans is selling flashlights that don't need a battery. He buys them for $2.50 in lots of 1,000. Then he sells them to the Boy Scouts for $4.00 each. They in turn sell them for $7.00 to their friends and neighbors. Who is the retail customer? Who is the wholesale buyer? Who is the middleman?

7. What percentage profit did Mr. Evans make over the price he paid? What percentage profit did the Boy Scouts make over the price they paid? Percentage-wise, did Mr. Evans or the Boy Scouts have the higher profit?

BIBLE AND DISCUSSION QUESTIONS

8. What is Paul's advice to those to whom God has granted the power to prosper?

9. Which concept in the study on "Clothed" was most helpful and encouraging to you?

10. Ask your parents if they know what the words "brick and mortar" mean to them.

Worksheet 8.1

Practice Questions

1. What are the biggest advantages for you to have a credit card?

2. What are some of the disadvantages that make you pause and be careful?

3. How do credit card companies make money?

4. What are the four largest and most well-known cards?

5. Why do some establishments have two prices, cash and credit?

6. Why is it difficult to secure your first credit card?

7. What are two typical requirements before you can have plastic in your wallet?

Bible and Discussion Questions

8. When does God ask us to test Him and His ability to meet our every need? What scripture reveals this promise?

9. Describe the difference between feeling convicted and feeling condemned.

10. Do your mom and dad have department store cards, or major credit cards, or both?

Worksheet 8.2

8.2

Practice Questions

1. What are a few large retail establishments where you shop that offer credit cards?

2. What are some of the potential pitfalls of using a debit card?

3. What is a "hold" that may be placed on your debit card when you are putting gas into your vehicle with a debit card?

4. If you had a debit card, how would you use it to avoid the common fees and pitfalls?

5. What does it mean to compare apples to apples when considering different credit card offers?

6. What is a credit score?

7. What habits or strategies can you develop to build your credit score?

BIBLE AND DISCUSSION QUESTIONS

8. Why does Steve prefer the language “return the tithe” instead of paying or giving a tenth?

9. What is the fruit, or result, of conviction that leads to repentance?

10. Why do your folks have the credit cards that they do?

Worksheet 8.3

8.3

Practice Questions

1. List two advantages of having a credit card.

2. What is one positive aspect of using a debit card?

3. What is a credit utilization ratio?

4. Should you strive to maintain a high or low ratio to boost your credit score?

5. How is dating or courting like enhancing your credit score?

6. What is a perk or reward offered for having some credit cards?

7. How is a secured card similar to a debit card?

BIBLE AND DISCUSSION QUESTIONS

8. What is the essential message or summation of 1 Chronicles 29:9–16?

9. Which King grievously sinned yet was wonderfully restored? Which Psalm is his prayer?

10. Do any of your family's plastic cards have rebates or perks that make them attractive?

Worksheet 8.4

Practice Questions

1. Explain the difference between a credit card and a debit card.

2. What is another positive aspect of having a credit card?

3. What is a joint account? What is a potential problem with having one?

4. According to the Northwestern Mutual 2018 Planning and Progress Study, what was the average debt reported Americans who took the survey in 2018?

5. What was the leading source of debt for older millennials?

6. What is another expression that is often used for an overdraft?

7. Explain why there is a penalty charged for an overdraft.

BIBLE AND DISCUSSION QUESTIONS

8. What is the difference between tithes and offerings (contributions)?

9. How would you describe the distinction between guilt and shame?

10. How did your dad and mom acquire their first credit card?

Worksheet 9.1

Practice Questions

1. What does Steve mean when he says to compare apples to apples? Please give an example.

2. What is the cost per mile of operating a car?

Use the comparison chart in your instructions for the next 5 questions.
For this buying expedition, I need two dozen eggs, a gallon of 2% milk, and 55 ounces of Honey Nut Cheerios. Since the different sizes make this hard to compare, compute by using the price per ounce without taking into consideration the size of the container.

3. Where is the best place to purchase eggs?

4. Which is the best place to buy these three products, Stauffers or Target?

5. Which is the best place to buy these three products, the Grocery Outlet or Costco?

6. Which store has the best price per ounce of yogurt?

7. Which items can't I purchase at the Sheetz Store?

BIBLE AND DISCUSSION QUESTIONS

8. What does it mean to do "all to the glory of God?" (1 Corinthians 10:31)

9. How do other committed believers help us in our walk with God?

10. What are your mom's and dad's favorite passages about forgiveness?

Worksheet 9.2

9.2

PRACTICE QUESTIONS

1. What are some other factors which add to the price of an item when shopping for the best price?

2. What did Steve observe while watching his parents seek to save pennies with coupons?

Use the comparison chart in your instructions for the next five questions.

3. When you quickly compare the cost of pizza, who do you think has the best price?

4. Figure out the lowest price per square inch of pizza.

5. If you are driving to buy enough pizza to feed your family of six, and are adding the cost of transportation, which is the best place to get the pizza?

6. Your family discovered you are driving for pizza and asked you to get four pounds of apples and two gallons of milk as well. Does this affect your answer to #5?

7. If Sheetz carried apples at $1.50 per pound, would this have impacted the answer to #6?

BIBLE AND DISCUSSION QUESTIONS

8. Why did Steve feel his view of work and ministry was unbiblical and unbalanced?

9. Which of the "one another" passages do you like the most? Why?

10. Ask your parents for their insights and thoughts on letting their light shine and being citizens of heaven.

Worksheet 9.3

Practice Questions

1. Why does Steve caution you to not always trust your eyes? Give an example please.

2. What are some benefits of shopping at a buying club?

Use the comparison chart in your instructions for the next 5 questions.

3. Who has the best price per ounce for Honey Nut Cheerios?

4. What are the two stores who have the best price per ounce for Almond Butter?

5. Which stores have the lowest price for eggs?

On this shopping expedition you need the following items: five pounds of apples, twelve ounces of cinnamon, and two gallons of milk. Since the different sizes make this hard to compare, compute by using the price per ounce without taking into consideration the size of the container.

6. What is the transportation expense to each store?

7. Which store in #5 do you think is the best place to shop? Why?

BIBLE AND DISCUSSION QUESTIONS

8. What characteristics do you think citizens of heaven possess?

9. Jesus sent out the first apostles two by two. The Holy Spirit continued this practice as He always sent Paul with someone. How many companions did Paul labor with? Name them please.

10. What are your grandparents' insights into discerning the difference between conviction and condemnation?

Worksheet 9.4

Practice Questions

1. What are some negative aspects of a buying club?

2. What do you have to be careful about when buying larger quantities of perishable foodstuffs?

Use the comparison chart in the instructions for the next five questions.
On this shopping expedition, you plan to visit four grocery stores and CVS, purchasing the following items: 2.5 pounds of coconut oil, 48 ounces of yogurt, and 1 pound of almond butter. Since the different sizes make this hard to compare, compute by using the price per ounce (rounded to cents) without taking into consideration the size of the container.

3. How many ounces are there in one pound?

4. Which store did you choose? Why?

5. Why would you buy groceries in a CVS Pharmacy?

6. Which store has the best buy for cinnamon?

7. What is a discount grocery store? Do you have any near your home?

BIBLE AND DISCUSSION QUESTIONS

8. Do you think it is more spiritual to be a pastor or a plumber? Why?

9. What are some other helpful and edifying benefits of being together with members of the family of God?

10. Where do your folks do most of their grocery shopping? Why do they shop there?

Worksheet 10.1

PRACTICE QUESTIONS

1. What are some intangibles that need to be considered in addition to lower cost?

2. If he has a choice, why does Steve like to buy local?

3. What are some positive aspects of buying at the local Bomberger Store that Steve has observed?

4. Which intangibles attracts Steve to SWA, even without considering the cost savings?

5. How much will it cost Steve to cut his grass for three years (including the cost of the mower)?

6. How much would it have cost to pay a lawn service to cut their grass for the same three years?

7. When looking for an auto mechanic, what characteristics does Steve look for?

Bible and Discussion Questions

8. Who created the concept of work?

9. Which of the first stanzas from the two hymns touched your heart?

10. What do your parents value when choosing a bank, a mechanic, or when purchasing an item?

Worksheet 10.2

Practice Questions

1. What is a warranty?

2. Which tools have an outstanding reputation due to their lifetime guarantee?

3. What are some benefits of caring for their lawn that Steve and John have discovered?

4. Steve still had the same mower in 2018 that he purchased nine years ago in 2010. If that mower were to have to be replaced this year, with all the information given in the Instruction Text, calculate how much money Steve has spent per year. Include the cost of replacing the battery twice, at a cost of $50.00 each time.

5. Based on the information in #4, what was the average cost of mowing the grass each time?

6. In researching the possibility of buying an electric bicycle, how many sources of information did Steve consider?

7. Whom do you consult for reliable information, or network with, before making a decision to buy something costly?

BIBLE AND DISCUSSION QUESTIONS

8. What impact did the fall of Adam and Eve have on work?

9. When did Daniel and David pray?

10. What experiences have your parents or grandparents had with guarantees and warranties?

Worksheet 10.3

10.3

PRACTICE QUESTIONS

1. Where do your folks take their vehicles to be repaired? Why do they like this particular place? How did they find it?

2. How many electronic items does your family own?

3. What percentage of these items were purchased new and did they come with a warranty?

4. What are your parent's thoughts about buying local versus purchasing online?

5. How much does it cost to fly via ACME AIR to Tampa from Baltimore with 1 bag, 1 carry-on, and an aisle seat?

6. What is the cost to make the same flight on GAMMA GO and SWA?

7. When might it be cost effective to fly on ACME instead of SWA?

Bible and Discussion questions

8. How does Math-U-See provide a service? Who benefits from this cooperative work?

9. What is your favorite prayer verse?

10. How do your parents network when making expensive purchases?

Worksheet 10.4

Practice Questions

1. Why does Steve like his local bank?

2. What are some advantages of shopping online?

3. Compare the cost of flying on all three carriers if you had one carry-on bag and took whichever seat the airline gave you. Who is the lowest price?

4. GAMMA GO charges $40.00 to check a second bag. How much would it be to fly with no carry-on, an aisle seat, and two bags to check on each airline?

5. Which airlines have the lowest and highest cancellation fees?

6. Steve is extra careful and willing to pay a little extra when purchasing which two items?

7. Which adjectives does he use in describing what he looks for when investing in these two important items?

BIBLE AND DISCUSSION QUESTIONS

8. Where is the Garden of Eden for Steve and Sandi? How do they tend it to the glory of God?

9. What does ACTS represent?

10. What are your parents' experiences when shopping for the best value in airline travel?

Worksheet 11.1

Practice Questions

1. Why do you need a car?

2. What are at least three alternative ways of getting around without a car?

3. What is the first thing Steve recommends you do when looking for a vehicle to purchase?

4. In Steve's opinion, why are most used cars being sold?

5. Where are a few places to look for a good used vehicle?

6. What are the ownership costs for a Ford F-150 for the first three years? How much is this per day?

7. What is the cost per mile of owning this same vehicle for three years?

Bible and discussion questions

8. What is the main point of the 1 Timothy 5:8?

9. Why does Steve refer to Luke 11:1–4 as the Disciple's Prayer instead of the Lord's Prayer?

10. What does this passage mean to you? "Hear, my son, your father's instruction, and forsake not your mother's teaching, for they are a graceful garland for your head and pendants for your neck." (Proverbs 1:8–9)

Worksheet 11.2

PRACTICE QUESTIONS

1. How long did Steve research the car he eventually purchased on EBAY? Why did he contact his mechanic friend and pay him $100.00 for his time?

2. Where can you find information on the history of a car or truck online?

3. Which sedan is generally one of the best-selling cars in America year after year?

4. Why are the fees so high for the first year of owning the new Ford F-150?

5. Why are ownership costs so easily forgotten?

6. What are the costs to own a Ford F-150 for the first two years? How much is this per week?

7. What is the cost per mile of owning this same vehicle for two years?

Bible and Discussion Questions

8. According to Scripture, who is responsible for providing for the basic needs of a family?

9. How does Jesus teach us NOT to pray?

10. Who do your parents consult when looking for a new or used vehicle? Why?

Worksheet 11.3

Practice Questions

1. What is a "private party" in the context of buying a used car?

2. How did your folks acquire their first three cars?

3. What lessons did they learn from these early experiences of owning a car?

4. Why has Steve never purchased a new car?

5. Given the table of data for a five-year period, do you understand why it can be a good investment to purchase a one or two year old vehicle?

6. What are the costs to own a Ford F-150 for the first four years? How much is this per month?

7. What is the cost per mile of owning this same vehicle for four years?

Bible and Discussion Questions

8. What does it mean to "give honor to whom honor is due"? How could you apply that passage from Romans 13:7?

9. How does Steve employ the "Disciple's Prayer" for his family?

10. How much was the first vehicle your mom, or dad purchased?

Worksheet 11.4

Practice Questions

1. What year was Steve's current 2015 Ford Explorer probably first sold?

2. Why does Steve think this car is a good bargain?

3. Before he made the final decision to buy it, what two things did he do?

4. What is appreciation? What things generally appreciate in value?

5. How does depreciation relate to vehicles?

6. What are the costs to own a Ford F-150 for the first five years? How much is this per day?

7. What is the cost per mile of owning this same vehicle for five years?

Bible and discussion questions

8. How did Paul set an example for the church in Thessalonica?

9. What is your favorite portion of the expanded prayer which Jesus gave to us?

10. Ask your grandparents for stories about their experience buying used cars.

Worksheet 12.1

Practice Questions

1. Your odometer reads 87,765 when you last filled up the tank. After driving a week and a half, you notice the gauge shows about a quarter of a tank left. The odometer now reads 87,959. When you refill the tank, it takes 12.6 gallons. What is your miles per gallon?

2. What lesson did Steve learn by keeping a record of the expenses while driving the red VW and the gold Plymouth?

3. What is one advantage of owning a brand-new car?

4. What is a downside of owning a new vehicle?

5. If you do become the owner of an older car, what will you need to set aside money for?

6. Generally, what is a good ballpark figure for the average cost per mile to operate a vehicle?

7. What is depreciation?

Bible and discussion questions

8. Which passages does Paul refer to when making his point in 1 Timothy 5:17–18?

9. What did God see in David that led to him being chosen to be the next king?

10. How often do your folks perform routine maintenance like changing their oil?

Worksheet 12.2

Practice Questions

1. How do you calculate mpg, or miles per gallon, for a vehicle?

2. On your last family vacation, your dad filled the tank the night before the trip, and the odometer read 54,183. When you arrived at the beach six hours later, you refilled the tank with 17.3 gallons of gas and the odometer now reads 54,532. What was your mpg for the day?

3. What is an approximate cost per mile for a horse and buggy?

4. If you ride from Harrisburg to Pittsburgh on a Greyhound bus, what is the cost per mile?

5. If you drive from Harrisburg to Pittsburgh on the PA Turnpike, without EZ Pass, what is your cost per mile just for tolls and fuel? Assume that you get 26 mpg.

6. Since your friend is doing the driving, how much should you and your three other friends consider chipping in for the trip?

7. What is the difference between operating expense and ownership cost?

Bible and Discussion Questions

8. What is Steve's advice to pastors or ministers who are offered a home owned by the church as part of their compensation? Why?

9. What attracted Samuel as he was looking for the next king among Jesse's sons?

10. What kind of gas mileage does your family car get?

Worksheet 12.3

Practice Questions

1. On October 3 you filled the gas tank with the odometer at 72,150. Over the next few weeks, you didn't stop to make any calculations but remember that you bought $20.00, $15.00, $25.00, and $12.00 worth of gas. Assuming the cost of gas is $3.00 per gallon, how many gallons of gas did you use?

2. What was your mpg over that time frame if the odometer now reads 72,606?

3. What are the total operating expenses for driving the Ford F-150 in year 4?

4. How does the answer to #3 compare to the operating expenses in year 2? Why is there a difference?

5. What were the total operating expenses for driving the Ford F-150 for the first three years?

6. How much does the answer to #5 work out per mile?

7. What type of insurance is required by law in most states?

Bible and discussion questions

8. How were the priests to be supported in the Old Testament?

9. What does scripture teach is the connection between the heart and the tongue?

10. What kinds of auto insurance do your parents carry? (collision, liability, etc.)?

Worksheet 12.4

Practice Questions

1. James drove 2,796 miles from Los Angeles to New York City in a Toyota Prius. He used 52.5 gallons of gas for the whole trip. What was his mpg for this cross-country expedition?

2. If Abigail bought the Ford F-150 new and kept it for four years, what was her average cost per mile for operating expenses?

3. According to the data in our chart, which is more costly in Year 1, operating expenses or ownership costs?

4. According to the data in our chart, which is more costly in Year 5, operating expenses or ownership costs? Why?

5. What is the cost per mile to fly to Pittsburgh from Harrisburg?

6. What is one positive and one negative aspect of taking the train to Pittsburgh?

7. When would you NOT consider carrying collision coverage on a used car?

Bible and Discussion Questions

8. As a member of a church, how should you seek to support your pastor or minister?

9. What is hypocrisy? Do we see it more quickly in others or ourselves?

10. What is the difference between highway miles per gallon and "driving around town" miles per gallon on your family car?

Worksheet 13.1

Practice Questions

For numbers 1–5: You have signed an agreement with your bank to borrow $180,000 with a 10% down payment for 30 years at a rate of 4.75%.

1. How much is your down payment? What is the amount of the loan?

2. Find the monthly payment.

3. What is the interest payment for the first month?

4. How much total interest will you pay during the life of this mortgage?

5. What effect would adding $50.00 as an extra monthly payment have on the mortgage?

6. Find the monthly payment for this mortgage in number using the formula. Round your figures to hundred-thousandths to find an approximate answer and see how it compares to the loan calculator.

7. Which part of this lesson was the most interesting?

Bible and discussion questions

8. What are three reasons Steve is saving money for the future?

9. Who advised Solomon to seek and ask God for wisdom?

10. Have your parents bought a house? If so, ask them about their first mortgage.

Worksheet 13.2

Practice Questions

For numbers 1–5: You have signed an agreement with your bank to borrow $250,000 with a 5% down payment for 20 years at an annual rate of 4.25%.

1. How much is your down payment? What is the amount of the loan?

2. Find the monthly payment.

3. What is the interest payment for the first month?

4. How much total interest will you pay during the life of this mortgage?

5. What effect would adding $100.00 as an extra monthly payment have on the mortgage?

6. Find the monthly payment for this mortgage in number using the formula. Round your figures to hundred-thousandths to find an approximate answer and see how it compares to the loan calculator.

7. Which aspect of this lesson is the most sobering?

Bible and discussion questions

8. What are Steve's plans for retirement?

9. What was David's prayer for his son Solomon?

10. What advice do your folks have about buying a house? Who was their real estate agent?

Worksheet 13.3

Practice Questions

For numbers 1–5: You have signed an agreement with your bank to borrow $140,000 with a 20% down payment for 15 years at an annual rate of $4\frac{1}{8}$%.

1. How much is your down payment? What is the amount of the loan?

2. Find the monthly payment.

3. What is the interest payment for the first month?

4. How much total interest will you pay during the life of this mortgage?

5. What effect would adding $25.00 as an extra payment have on the mortgage?

6. How much is the monthly interest rate for a $5\frac{3}{4}$% loan? Round to thousandths.

7. Which will have a lower interest rate, a 30 year mortgage or a 15 year mortgage?

BIBLE AND DISCUSSION QUESTIONS

8. What was the impact of the prodigal son reaching his inheritance hastily at the beginning?

9. What three specific commands were given to the kings of Israel?

10. If your parents have a mortgage, where did they secure it?

Worksheet 13.4

Practice Questions

For numbers 1–5: You have signed an agreement with your bank to borrow $195,000 with a 10% down payment for 30 years at an annual rate of $4\frac{3}{4}$%.

1. How much is your down payment? What is the amount of the loan?

2. Find the monthly payment.

3. What is the interest payment for the first month?

4. How much total interest will you pay during the life of this mortgage?

5. What effect would adding $125.00 as an extra monthly payment have on the mortgage?

6. What is a lien?

7. What are mortgage points? How much do they cost?

Bible and discussion questions

8. What is the ultimate priceless inheritance Steve wants to leave for his children?

9. How does the life of Solomon influence Steve?

10. What are your grandparents thoughts about owning a home and retirement?

Worksheet 14.1

Practice Questions

1. How do you compute the transfer taxes and title insurance in the example in this lesson?

2. If the purchase price of the house on the chart was $300,000, what would be the cost of the fixed fees?

3. What is PMI and why do the Jacksons have to pay it each month?

4. How much did the Hills save each month by making a larger down payment?

5. Compare the total interest paid on each of the mortgages for the Jacksons and Hills on their amortization tables. Who paid more and by how much?

6. How much did the Hills save by not making PMI payments over a 10-year period?

7. What is good faith or earnest money?

Bible and Discussion Questions

8. What is one unique component of living by faith which God led Hudson Taylor and George Müller to practice?

9. What is the "heart" of a man in the Bible?

10. Did your parents rent a home before buying their own place? What did they think of the experience?

Worksheet 14.2

14.2

Practice Questions

1. What is escrow?

2. What are prepaid reserves?

3. Who receives escrow payments from the monthly payment? Why?

4. What service does a title company do for a buyer?

5. Why do you need title insurance?

6. What are the most expensive costs of a closing?

7. What do experts advise about how much you should be spending each month on your housing costs?

BIBLE AND DISCUSSION QUESTIONS

8. What is the amazing promise found in Matthew 6:33?

9. How is God's heart revealed in Deuteronomy 5:29?

10. Do you or your parents know any more advantages or disadvantages for renting versus owning beyond those listed in this lesson?

Worksheet 14.3

PRACTICE QUESTIONS

State	Monthly Mortgage Payment	Monthly Rent
Alabama	995	1,010
Hawaii	2,750	2,200
Illinois	1,150	1,625
Montana	1,500	1,175
Pennsylvania	1,008	1,374

1. In which state(s) would it be more cost effective to rent a place?

2. In which state(s) would it be more cost effective to own a house?

3. Do any of these states have similar costs to rent or own?

4. Out of the 50 states in the US, what percentage of them lean towards home ownership?

5. How does the cost of closing or settlement fees impact your decision to rent or own?

6. What are some reasons for owning instead of renting, besides cost considerations?

7. What percentage of the cost of a home do folks suggest you set aside for maintenance and repairs each year?

Bible and discussion questions

8. Where in his letters to the churches did Paul mention and solicit funds for the poor?

9. What is the relationship between our heart and our treasure?

10. If your folks are willing, ask them what they spend each month, on average, on utilities.

Worksheet 14.4

Practice Questions

1. How do most people save for retirement?

2. What is equity?

3. What are some reasons for renting instead of owning?

4. How much interest did the Tortoise earn on his investment over 10 years?

5. What lesson did the Hare learn when he saw how much the Tortoise had accumulated?

6. What advice did the title professional have for the students taking this class?

7. Have you begun to save for a home in the future?

Bible and discussion questions

8. What was the balance which God taught Steve about living by faith and working?

9. What did Steve do when he discovered he had a hard heart?

10. If your folks are willing, ask them what they spend each quarter on other bills like water, sewer, or trash removal.

Worksheet 14.5

Practice Questions

The Peters clan decides to buy a $150,000 home. They are making a down payment of 10% for 20 years and receive a $4\frac{3}{8}$% mortgage. Using the numbers and percentages from the first page in the instructions, estimate the following expenses if the fixed fees are the same.

1. Principal and Interest portion of the monthly payment

2. If the PMI is $110 and the PT and HI are $280, what will be the monthly payment?

3. How much of the monthly payment will be assigned to an escrow fund?

4. How much will be needed for the prepaid reserves?

5. What will be the transfer taxes and title insurance?

6. What are the estimated total closing costs?

7. In looking at the closing costs and fees, which expense surprised you? Why?

Bible and Discussion Questions

8. What is the essence of 2 Thessalonians 3:6-12?

9. In the sampling of the 862 verses about the heart, which one touched your heart?

10. If your folks are willing, ask them what they spend each year on property taxes.

Worksheet 15.1

Practice Questions

1. How much coverage is there in a gallon of paint on a smooth surface?

2. How many square feet are in a square (as in shingles or siding)?

3. What kind of jobs around the home can you do yourself?

4. How many pieces of 12 ft 6 in by 8 in siding are needed to be in a carton that contains 200 square feet?

5. Why does Steve think it is a good financial decision to buy quality materials and not try to skimp on the cost of paint?

Figure 1

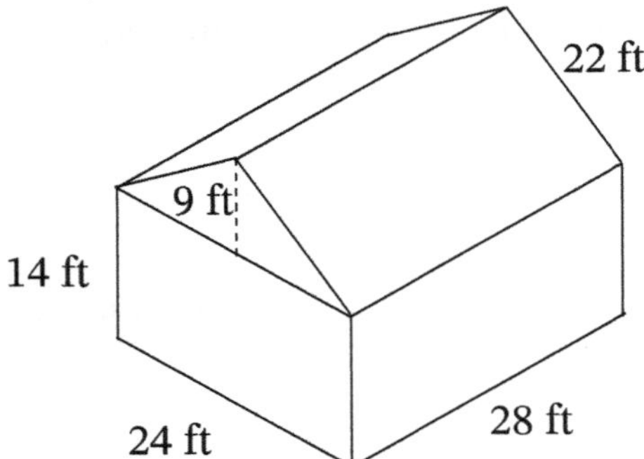

6. Calculate how many cartons of siding are needed to cover the sides in figure 1.

7. How many squares of shingles are needed to roof this home in figure 1?

Bible and Discussion Questions

8. Why are matters of money so important to a married couple?

9. How was the Holy Spirit present at the incarnation or birth of Jesus?

10. Which maintenance jobs does your family do for your home?

Worksheet 15.2

Practice Questions

1. In what areas of home maintenance or simple construction do you think it is important to hire an expert?

2. What is the difference between an estimate and a bid? Why should you get estimates and bids in writing?

3. What are five tips to remember when talking to a contractor?

4. How much paint is needed to paint the walls in a living room that is 15 feet by 14 feet with walls that are 8.5 feet high? The walls are pretty clean, and only need one coat to spruce up the room. If paint is $21.00 per quart or $54.00 per gallon, what is the most economical way to purchase the paint? How much is the total cost?

5. How much paint will you need to paint the ceiling with two coats? If ceiling paint is $17.50 per quart or $42.00 per gallon, what is the most economical way to purchase the paint and how much is the total cost?

Figure 2

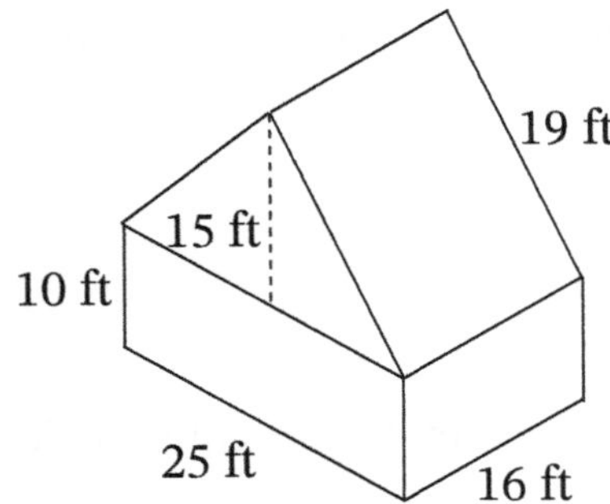

6. Calculate how many squares of siding are needed to cover the sides of the house in figure 2.

7. How many squares of shingles are needed to roof this home?

BIBLE AND DISCUSSION QUESTIONS

8. Is the husband always supposed to make the final financial decision? Why or why not?

9. Where in Isaiah did Jesus read, "The Spirit of the Lord is upon me, because He has anointed me"?

10. What simple construction projects are your parents comfortable doing?

Worksheet 15.3

Practice Questions

1. Sammy Sprayer is going to be painting your barn. He is working for time and materials and estimates he will use 20 gallons of paint, and that it will take him 26 hours at $33.00 per hour. He has an account with a quality paint store and can buy the paint for $34.00 per gallon. How much are you estimating it will cost to have Sammy spray your barn?

2. This week a sale flyer came in the mail from A-1 Hardware with a lower-quality house paint at $24.00 per gallon. You decide to provide the paint and just pay Sammy for his labor. How much are you saving on the cost of the paint?

3. After Sammy finished the barn, he realized it took him only 25 hours. He used 20 gallons of paint. With your materials and his labor, what was the total cost of the job?

4. Four years later the paint is weathered and cracking and needs to be redone. What was the cost per year to paint the barn?

5. While Sammy Sprayer was in your neighborhood, he painted another barn with his own materials. It also took 25 hours and 20 gallons of paint, but this job didn't have to be repainted for seven years. What was the price per year of this paint job? Does it pay to use lower quality materials?

Figure 3

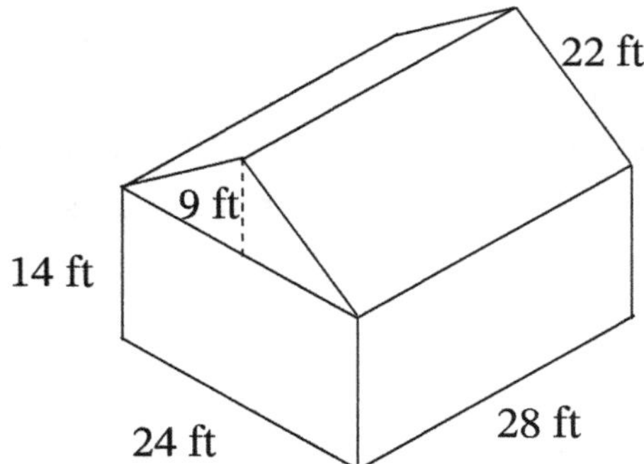

6. A better quality siding costs $150.00 per carton. How much will it cost to purchase the vinyl siding for this project in figure 3?

7. The corner pieces are $2.25 per linear foot and the top and bottom channel pieces are $0.50 per linear foot. How much does this add to the siding expense for materials?

BIBLE AND DISCUSSION QUESTIONS

8. How is the husband to love His wife? Who is the model husband?

9. Why can the appellation "Jesus the Christ" also be rendered "Jesus the Anointed?"

10. What advice do your folks have about home maintenance and do-it-yourself projects? Do they have any humorous anecdotes on this topic?

Worksheet 15.4

Practice Questions

1. Peter Painter visited a homeowner and gave him a fixed bid to paint his home. He arrived at this price by estimating 46 hours at $25.00 per hour and $175.00 for paint and other materials. Then he added 20% to this total just to be safe. How much was his bid?

2. After Peter had finished painting, his records showed he had actually worked 48 hours and spent $148.00 for paint and other materials. What was his actual cost?

3. What did Peter's hourly wage for the job turn out to be based on his original fixed bid? If you had agreed to pay him for his time and materials, how much would you have saved?

4. How much paint is needed to paint the walls of an attic that is 13.5 feet by 11.5 feet with walls that are only 6 feet high? This is the first time it has been painted, so it will need one primer coat to cover the new drywall and two finish coats. If primer is $15.00 per gallon and $6.50 per quart, how much is the cost for the first primer coat?

5. If paint is $38.00 per gallon and $15.50 per quart for the finish paint, how much is the cost for two coats?

Figure 4

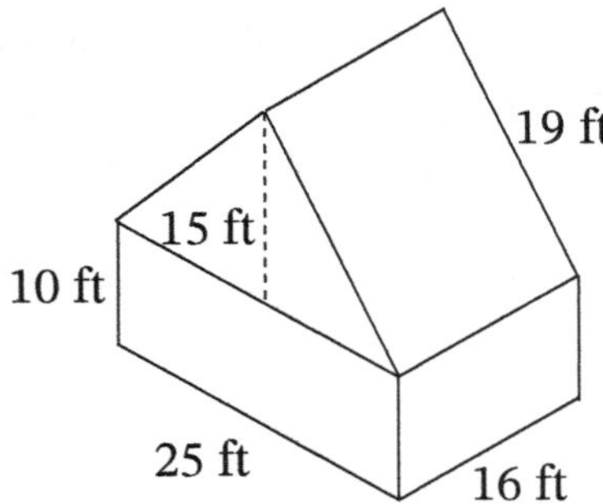

6. Vinyl siding is $130.00 per carton. How much will it cost to purchase the materials for this project in figure 4?

7. The corner pieces are $2.25 per linear foot and the top and bottom channel pieces are $0.50 per linear foot. How much does this add to the siding expense for materials.

BIBLE AND DISCUSSION QUESTIONS

8. Which principles govern how Steve thinks about marriage and treasure?

9. Why is to our advantage that Jesus ascended to sit at the right hand of the Father?

10. Ask your parents how they chose a contractor to work on your home and what they learned from the experience(s).

Worksheet 15.5

Practice Questions

1. What are some advantages to doing home improvements by yourself or as a family?

2. What do you think are the five most important tips to consider when hiring a contractor?

3. What kind of jobs around the home can you do yourself?

4. How much paint is needed to paint the walls of a bedroom that is 9 feet by 12 feet with walls that are 8 feet high? It will need two coats to cover the old paint. If paint is $19.00 per quart or $50.00 per gallon, what is the most economical way to purchase the paint? How much is the total cost?

5. How much paint will you need to paint the ceiling with two coats? If paint is $19.00 per quart or $50.00 per gallon, what is the most economical way to purchase the paint? How much is the total cost?

Figure 5

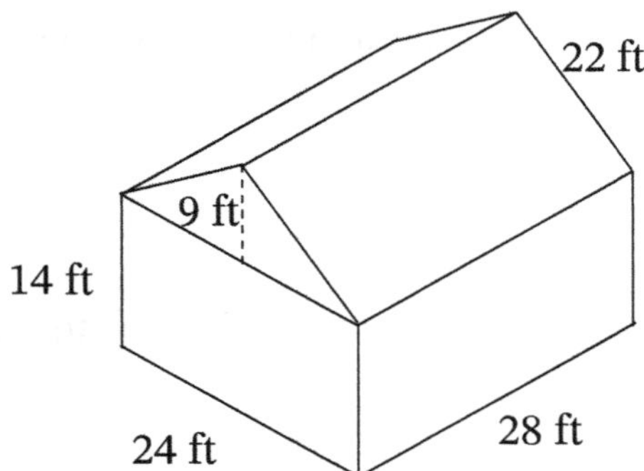

6. Instead of using siding, you decide to paint the exterior of your home (figure 5). If primer is $23.00 per gallon and $9.00 per quart, what is the cost for the first coat on your home?

7. The acrylic gloss finish paint you have chosen is $65.00 per gallon and $27.00 per quart. What is the cost for two finish coats on the outside of your home in figure 5?

BIBLE AND DISCUSSION QUESTIONS

8. What are some things you can do to develop a family budget?

9. What was the last recorded command of Jesus to the disciples?

10. What advice do your parents have about how to find a reputable contractor?

Worksheet 16.1

Practice Questions

1. Which is cheaper, 68¢ per square foot or $6.00 per square yard?

2. If the carpet costs $9.95 per yard, and the padding is 49¢ per foot, how much will it cost to carpet your 9 ft × 12 ft bedroom if you install it yourself?

3. Name two bargains Steve found when finishing the construction on his home.

4. If Steve needed 200 feet of trim to finish his doors and baseboard, how much did he save buying 6 ft pieces for $1.00 instead of 79¢ per foot?

5. How did Steve save money when renting a large moving truck?

6. Ada the quilter came to the fabric store and bought four yards of 54 inch flatfold material on sale at $1.99/yd. She then bought three more yards of 54 inch 100% cotton broadcloth at $5.89/yd. What was her total bill, including a local sales tax of 6%?

7. How many square yards of material did Ada buy?

Bible and Discussion Questions

8. Why should we pray about everything, even when buying things?

9. What are some things that the Spirit does in the life of a Christian?

10. Have your parents ever negotiated or haggled when purchasing some item or service?

Worksheet 16.2

Practice Questions

1. Joseph is attending a college that encourages students to wear a tuxedo for formal occasions. In addition, he is a member of the chorus and needs a tux for performances. This year there are three choral performances scheduled plus two formal gatherings. He can either rent a tux for $75.00 for each event or buy one for $250.00. What is the most economical course for Joseph?

2. Assuming Joseph buys a tuxedo, how many times does he need to put on his fancy tux before it pays for itself?

3. What are some of the disadvantages of borrowing a tool?

4. Stephanie the seamstress bought a fabric blend at $3.69 per yard. She purchased $7\frac{1}{2}$ yards of fabric blend. What was her final bill, including the 6% tax?

5. If the price of a yard of carpet is $15.00 per yard, installation is 60¢ per square foot, and padding is 90¢ per foot, find the cost of carpet for a room that is 12 feet by 18 feet.

6. How much is the whole cost of the carpet in #5 per square yard?

7. How much is the whole cost of the carpet in #5 per square foot?

Bible and Discussion Questions

8. What is the most meaningful Scripture in this section to you?

9. Which workings of the Spirit have you experienced?

10. What pearls of wisdom do your folks have for you about negotiating?

Worksheet 16.3

Practice Questions

1. What are the advantages of borrowing a tool?

2. What factors would incline you to borrow something versus owning it?

3. Billie Jo bought 20 yards of felt at $4.29 per yard. How much did it cost? How many square yards did Billie Jo purchase if the fabric was 72 inches wide?

4. Naomi the quilter came to the fabric store and bought five yards of 54 inch flatfold material on sale at $1.89/yd. She then bought five more yards of 54 inch 100% cotton broadcloth at $5.89/yd. What was her total bill with a sales tax of 5.5%?

5. How many square feet of material did Naomi buy?

6. Stephanie also bought a fabric blend at $3.79 per yard. She purchased 4 1/3 yards of fabric blend. What was her final bill with the 6.25% tax?

7. If the price of a yard of carpet is $18.00 per yard, installation is 70¢ per square foot and padding is 95¢ per foot, find the cost of carpet for a room that is 11 ft by 15 ft. Include the padding and the installation.

BIBLE AND DISCUSSION QUESTIONS

8. Steve describes God as a gentleman. What does this have to do with prayer?

9. How is the Holy Spirit connected with comprehending God's love? Which passage supports this thought?

10. What items does your family rent? When and why?

Worksheet 16.4

Practice Questions

1. What piece of equipment did Steve rent for a day, twice a year? Why did he rent it instead of buying it?

2. The carpet cleaner rents for $19.00 for four hours, $29.00 per day (24 hours), and $87.00 per week. The machine costs $1,200. How many daily rentals does a company have to rent a carpet cleaner before it pays for itself? How many weekly rentals would it take?

3. How many yards of carpet are needed to cover a room 20 ft. by 14 ft.?

4. Installation is $7.50 per square yard. What would it cost to do the room in #3?

5. Find the price for padding for the room in #3 if it costs 54¢ per square foot.

6. For numbers 4–5, what is the total cost for carpeting the room if the price of the carpet we chose is $16.50 per yard?

7. You are preparing a piece of ground for a garden, but you don't own a shovel. A new one costs $19.50, and you can rent one for $6.00 per day. You decide to borrow one from a buddy, and then you break it. After you replace the shovel for $19.50, what are you going to do next since you still need to prepare the ground in your garden?

Bible and Discussion Questions

8. Explain Joshua 9:3-6 in your own words.

9. What does "inspired" mean? Why do we say the Scriptures are inspired?

10. Ask your parents about some wonderful examples where God has blessed their purchases and multiplied their dollars.

Worksheet 16.5

Practice Questions

1. How do you find bargains?

2. What was Steve's first experience at bargaining?

3. Carpet costs $24.95 per yard. How much is that per square foot?

4. How much carpet and padding would you need for your living room if it is 14 ft by 18 ft? Carpet is $16.25 per yard and padding is $7.15 per yard. What is the total cost for the carpet you need?

5. How much will it cost to have the carpet installed in the same room if the installation cost is 85¢ per square foot?

6. Steve did some research and discovered 1 square foot of maple flooring costs $4.95 and it is an additional $4.00 per square foot to install it. His house was 2,600 square feet. What would the cost be to buy the flooring and have it installed?

7. Steve calculated that he spent an additional $700.00 for glue, stain, and polyurethane finish. How much did he invest in his floor including the cost of the maple? How much did he save by doing it himself?

Bible and Discussion Questions

8. How does God encourage us to ask Him to supply our needs?

9. What does the Spirit of truth do in John 15:26?

10. Now that you have acquired more knowledge of this subject, ask your grandparents about their experiences of negotiating as well as others situations where God has blessed their purchasing.

Worksheet 17.1

Practice Questions

1. What is the price for one yard of 3,000 grade concrete?

2. How many yards of poured concrete would you need for a driveway that is 12 ft by 60 ft and 6 inches deep?

3. How many truckloads would be required to transport the material for #2?

4. What would be the cost for the driveway in #2 if 4,000 grade was used?

5. Calculate the amount of concrete and the number of truckloads, for a patio 30 ft × 15 ft × 4 in.

6. What would be the cost for the patio in #5 using 3,500 grade concrete?

7. What percentage of a dry yard of standard concrete is cement?

Bible and Discussion Questions

8. Which verse encourages us that God provides for us and wants us to have good things to enjoy?

9. What title would Steve suggest for the fifth book in the New Testament?

10. How do your parents make decisions about making significant purchases?

Worksheet 17.2

Practice Questions

1. How many pounds of sand are needed to fill a sandbox that is 6 ft × 4 ft × 2 ft? Give the answer in tons as well.

2. How much concrete would you need for a driveway that is 14 ft by 85 ft and 8 inches deep?

3. How many truckloads would be required to transport the material for #2?

4. What would be the cost for the driveway in #2 with grade 4,500 concrete mix?

5. Calculate the amount of concrete, and the cost for a patio with 3,000 grade concrete that is 10 ft × 22 ft × 5 in.

6. What percentage of a standard dry yard of concrete is sand?

7. How many cubic feet of gravel are there in 6 and 1/4 tons?

Bible and Discussion Questions

8. What are several synonyms for covet?

9. How long was Jesus with the disciples after He rose from the dead and before he ascended?

10. How do your folks discern the difference between want and a need?

Worksheet 17.3

Practice Questions

For numbers 1–4: The highway department is replacing a section of road near the interstate highway. It is $\frac{1}{20}$ of a mile long by 15 ft wide and 1 ft deep. They are using 4,000 grade concrete.

1. How much concrete will they need? Round your answer to the nearest cubic yard and use this answer for numbers 2–4.

2. How much sand and gravel will be in this mix?

3. How many truckloads are needed to complete the task?

4. What will the expense be just for the concrete?

5. How many gallons of water are in one yard of wet concrete?

6. What percentage of a standard dry yard of concrete is crushed stone or gravel?

7. The water is not working in our home and I need to carry it in from the nearby stream. I am wanting to fill up a tub which is 2 ft by 5 ft and is 15 in deep. If I can carry two 40 lb buckets at a time, how many trips will I have to make?

Bible and Discussion Questions

8. After talking to God, who should be the next person to consult before making a major purchase?

9. Why didn't the disciples go to Bithynia? What is the name for the Holy Spirit in this same passage?

10. Have any of your family members had an occasion to buy gravel, sand, concrete, or water?

Worksheet 17.4

Practice Questions

1. Your mom would like a 5 ft by 30 ft concrete walkway which is 4 inches thick. How many cubic feet will this be?

2. How many yards of concrete is this patio going to require? Which grade of concrete would you recommend and what is the cost?

3. How much water will be needed for a round 12 ft diameter above ground swimming pool that is 3 ft deep? Round this answer to the nearest gallon and use that value for #4.

4. If you had to fill the pool with your hose and it flows at a rate of 24 gallons per minute, how many hours would it take you to fill the above ground pool in #3?

5. How many yards of gravel are there in 25 tons? Round to the nearest tenth.

6. Which weighs more, 4 yards of gravel or 185 cubic feet of water?

7. How many cubic feet are in 6,000 gallons of water?

Bible and Discussion Questions

8. Who did Steve consult before he purchased a new riding mower?

9. How do we know the Holy Spirit is a person? Give at least two Scriptures to support your answer.

10. Do you have discussions as a family about making major purchases like a new car or lawnmower?

Worksheet 17.5

Practice Questions

1. What is the difference between 3,000 grade and 5,000 grade concrete mix?

2. How many yards of gravel are there in 18 tons?

3. 275 cubic feet of sand weighs how many tons?

4. How many cubic feet are in 2,500 gallons of water?

For questions 5–7: Seth wanted to make a basketball court in his backyard that is 30 ft by 50 ft.

5. After digging the area for the court, he wanted a 3 in base of gravel before pouring the concrete on top. How many yards will he need? How many tons is this?

6. If gravel is $40 per ton, plus a $25 delivery charge, how much will this cost?

7. What grade of concrete do you recommend for this court? How much will that cost if it is 4 in thick according to the prices in the instruction text?

Bible and Discussion Questions

8. How does Proverbs 11:14 apply to making good decisions and wise purchases?

9. Name at least two human attributes of the Holy Spirit that were most interesting and revealing to you. What were they?

10. What was the most interesting thing you learned in this lesson?

Worksheet 18.1

Practice Questions

For numbers 1–2: Duct *A* is circular with a radius of 4 inches. Duct *B* is a rectangle that measures 6 inches by 8 inches. Please round your calculations to hundredths.

1. Which duct will let more air pass through it, Duct *A* or Duct *B*?

2. See if you can figure out which duct uses the most sheet metal.

3. How much electricity (amps) is used to power a 60-watt light bulb?

4. If you have a 50-amp service, what is your potential for wattage?

5. Calculate the safe capacity for a 20-amp breaker.

6. Could you safely operate a 1,050-watt toaster, four 100-watt light bulbs, and five 60-watt bulbs on the 20-amp breaker in #5?

7. Compute your bill for 750 kWh without the PA Tax Adj. Surcharges. Use the chart in the Instruction Manual under "My Electric Bill" without PA surcharges.

BIBLE AND DISCUSSION QUESTIONS

8. Why is Steve wary of free gifts?

9. Why was it important for Jesus to hear His Father's words at His baptism?

10. Which monthly utility bill is the largest in your home?

Worksheet 18.2

Practice Questions

For numbers 1–2: Duct *A* is circular with a diameter of 6 inches. Duct *B* is a rectangle that measures 4.5 inches by 7 inches. Please round your calculations to hundredths.

1. Which duct will let more air pass through it, Duct *A* or Duct *B*?

2. See if you can figure out which duct uses the most sheet metal.

3. How much electricity (amps) is used to power a 75-watt light bulb?

4. If you have a 30-amp service, what is your potential for wattage?

5. Calculate the safe capacity for a 30-amp breaker.

6. Could you safely operate two 500-watt refrigerators, an 800-watt microwave, and five 100-watt light bulbs on a 30-amp breaker?

7. Compute your bill for 1,500 kWh without the PA Tax Adj. Surcharges. Use the chart in the Instruction Manual under "My Electric Bill" without PA surcharges.

Bible and Discussion Questions

8. What does the saying, "haste makes waste" have to do with purchasing carefully?

9. How did Jesus respond to the false accusations of His enemy?

10. Does your family use gas, electric, wood, coal, or oil heat? Approximately how much is spent on electricity each month?

Worksheet 18.3

Practice Questions

For numbers 1–2: Duct *A* is a square with each side measuring 5 inches. Duct *B* is a rectangle that measures 4 inches by 6 inches. Please round your calculations to hundredths.

1. Which duct will allow more air to pass through it?

2. Which duct uses the most sheet metal?

3. How much electricity (amps) is used to power a 40-watt bulb?

4. If you have a 40-amp service, what is your safe capacity for wattage?

5. Calculate the safe capacity for a 15-amp breaker.

6. If you were already operating a 500-watt refrigerator and a 1,050-watt toaster, how many 40-watt light bulbs could be burning safely on a 15-amp breaker?

7. Using the chart in the instruction manual, compute a bill for 1,000 kWh of electricity without PA surcharges.

Bible and Discussion Questions

8. Why did the salespeople at the resort try so hard to convince Steve and Sandi to buy one of their lots that day?

9. Which Christians have been tempted to doubt they belong to God and are His adopted children?

10. Have you parents ever been tempted to respond to a slick sales pitch and buy something the first time they saw it without researching or taking time to consider it?

Worksheet 18.4

18.4

PRACTICE QUESTIONS

For numbers 1–2: Duct *A* is circular with a diameter of 5 inches. Duct *B* is a a square with each side measuring 4.5 inches. Please round your calculations to hundredths.

1. Which duct will allow more air to pass through it?

2. Which duct requires the most sheet metal to build it?

3. How much electricity (amps) is used to power a 25-watt light bulb? Round your answer to the nearest hundredth.

4. If you have a 75-amp service, what is your potential for wattage?

5. See if you can figure the safe capacity for a 20-amp breaker.

6. If you are operating a toaster on a 20-amp breaker, how many 60-watt light bulbs could also be used safely?

7. Ask your folks if you can read last month's electric bill. Compute the average price you are paying for one kWh of electricity.

Bible and Discussion Questions

8. What is one negative and one positive of owning a timeshare?

9. Does God love and enjoy you? Which scriptures support your answer?

10. What advice do your folks have about meditating on scripture about our identity in Christ?

Worksheet 18.5

Practice Questions

1. What makes a breaker flip or break?

2. What is safe capacity? How does it differ from maximum capacity?

3. What does HVAC represent?

4. Which variable measures how fast the electrons are flowing through wire?

5. Most homes in the U. S. have a ______ amp service.

6. What is the name for the pusher of the electrons that increases the speed of the current?

7. What is a kWh?

Bible and Discussion Questions

8. When does Steve think it is okay to purchase quickly?

9. I hope these verses about who you are in Christ are an encouragement to you. Which one(s) did you like the best?

10. Ask your grandparents what advice they have about purchasing carefully.

Worksheet 19.1

Practice Questions

1. What are the actual dimensions of a 4 × 6?

2. What are the dimensions of a board called a one-by-four?

3. Calculate the height and width of a stack of four 4 × 4s.

4. What is the R-value of a 2 × 6 wall filled with cellulose?

5. What is the R-value of a 2 × 6 wall with 1.5 inches of foam insulation and the rest filled with cellulose?

6. What color is the Pink Panther?

7. Twenty liters is how many gallons? Round to tenths in the final answer.

BIBLE AND DISCUSSION QUESTIONS

8. What are three ways God speaks to us when we ask for guidance?

9. What is the distinction Steve makes between knowing facts about God and knowing God personally?

10. What are the dimensions of the rafters in your ceiling? What kind of insulation is there in your attic?

Worksheet 19.2

Practice Questions

1. What is a board called that measures $1\frac{1}{2}$ inches by $5\frac{1}{2}$ inches called?

2. What are the dimensions of a six-by-six?

3. Calculate the height of a stack of four 2×4s stacked on their wide sides.

4. Find the R-value of a 2×10 wall filled with fiberglass insulation.

5. Find the R-value of a 2×8 wall with 1.75 inches of foam insulation, and the rest of the space filled with fiberglass insulation.

6. What is the R-value of 12 inches of cellulose blown into the attic?

7. How many meters in one mile?

Bible and discussion questions

8. What kind of feeling or sensing can we expect if we are on the right track? Give a scripture that supports this thought.

9. In the list of scriptures under "What I Know," which one do you identify with the most?

10. What are the dimensions of the thickness of the walls in your home? What kind of insulation is in them?

Worksheet 19.3

Practice Questions

1. What is the board called that measures $\frac{3}{4}$ inches by $5\frac{1}{2}$ inches?

2. What are the dimensions of a two-by-eight?

3. Calculate the width of the following boards lying side by side: one 2 × 4, one 2 × 6, and two 2 × 8s.

4. If an entire 2 × 6 wall cavity is filled with foam insulation, what is the R-value?

5. What is the R-value of a 2 × 4 wall with one inch of foam and the rest filled with cellulose?

6. Find the R-value of a ceiling with 2 by 10 rafters filled with two inches of foam insulation and the remaining space filled with cellulose.

7. One square mile is how many square kilometers?

Bible and Discussion Questions

8. What is the difference between leading sheep and leading goats?

9. What has Steve experienced on his daily walks the past few years?

10. Has your family ever installed insulation themselves? What did they think of the experience?

Worksheet 19.4

Practice Questions

1. What are the real dimensions of a four-by-four?

2. What is the name of the board that is $\frac{3}{4}$ inches by $3\frac{1}{2}$ inches?

3. Calculate the height of a stack of the following boards: three 1 × 4s, two 2 × 4s, and one 4 × 4.

4. Find the R-value of a 2 × 8 wall filled with fiberglass insulation.

5. Find the R-value of a 2 × 8 ceiling with 1.5 inches of polyurethane foam, and the rest of the space filled with blown-in cellulose.

6. What is the R-value of a 2 × 10 wall filled with 2.5 inches of foam insulation and the remaining space with fiberglass batts?

7. What are the dimensions of a two-by-four in centimeters? Round the answer to hundredths.

BIBLE AND DISCUSSION QUESTIONS

8. Does God communicate the same way to each of us? Give two examples of how God spoke differently to men in the Bible.

9. Why does Matthew 7:21-23 challenge and convict Steve?

10. What advice do your parents have for making a financial decision after you have researched, asked questions, and prayed?

Worksheet 19.5

Practice Questions

1. What are the real dimensions of a two-by-four?

2. What is the name of the board that is $3\frac{1}{2}$ inches by $5\frac{1}{2}$ inches?

3. Calculate the width of the following boards lying side by side: two 4 × 4s, three 1 × 6s, and one 2 × 10.

4. If the entire 2 × 4 wall cavity is filled with foam, what is the R-value?

5. Which has the highest R value, a 2 × 4 with polyurethane foam or a 2 × 10 wall filled with cellulose insulation?

6. What is the R-value of a 2 × 6 wall filled with 1 inch of foam insulation if the rest of the space is filled with cellulose?

7. How many kilometers in a 3.1 mile race? Round to tenths please. What is this race called?

Bible and discussion questions

8. How did God communicate to Elijah?

9. If we know Jesus, do we know the Father as well? Support your answer with a scripture, please.

10. What advice do your grandparents have for making a financial decision after you have researched, asked questions, and prayed?

Worksheet 20.1

Practice Questions

1. Sarah bought a snack for $1.45. She paid for it with a five-dollar bill. What is the correct change and how will Mercy count it back to Sarah?

2. Cyrus bought a sharp knife for $3.64 and paid for it with a ten-dollar bill. What is the correct change and how will Ernest count it back to Cyrus?

3. Where are three places in your neighborhood to find good sales?

4. Quickly estimate the temperature in Fahrenheit if it is 25° Celsius.

5. Now compute the accurate equivalent of 25°C in F.

6. Your odometer says you are going 90 kph. How fast is that in mph? Use your ratios to estimate. Round to a whole number.

7. Check your answer with a precise conversion on your phone or computer.

Bible and Discussion Questions

8. What is the difference between a tithe and a contribution?

9. What characteristics do you see in the father in Luke 15?

10. Where are some places that your family has made contributions?

Worksheet 20.2

Practice Questions

1. Darby bought lunch for $9.20. She paid for it with a twenty-dollar bill. What is the correct change and how will Chloe count it back to Darby?

2. Faith bought a jacket for $35.31 and paid for it with a fifty-dollar bill. What is the correct change and how will Maddie count it back to Faith?

3. Give Seth two tips for saving money when he is eating out.

4. Using the quick method, estimate the temperature in Fahrenheit if it is 37°C.

5. Now compute the exact Fahrenheit equivalent of 37°C.

6. The sign says you are 75 miles away from the border. How many kilometers is that? Estimate with your ratios.

7. Check your answer with a precise conversion on your phone or computer.

Bible and discussion questions

8. Who is your neighbor? Can you think of someone who would fit into this category that you could serve or support prayerfully or financially?

9. There are 30 verses about God and what He has done for us. In the first 10, choose one which you liked the best and write it out.

10. Are there missionaries that your family supports either by prayer and/or financially? How did they sense God directing them to give in this way?

Worksheet 20.3

Practice Questions

1. Isaac purchased a chicken sandwich at the drive through for $3.58. He paid for it with a five-dollar bill. What is the correct change and how will Rachel count it back to Isaac at the window?

2. Teagan bought breakfast for $6.09 and paid for it with a ten-dollar bill. What is the correct change and how will Maggie count it back to Teagan at the register?

3. Collin is frugal. Can you think of two places where he can find bargains online or in the paper?

4. Quickly estimate the temperature in Fahrenheit if it is 15° Celsius.

5. Now compute the accurate equivalent of 15°C in F.

6. The back seat drivers say you need to speed up. The odometer reads 60 kph. How many mph is this? Estimate with the unit multiplier ratios.

7. Check your answer with a precise conversion on your phone or computer.

Bible and discussion questions

8. What is religion that is pure and undefiled? Do you know anyone who fits this description?

9. In the second 10 passages, choose one which you liked the best and write it out.

10. Do your parents like to shop for bargains? If so, what are some great places your parents have discovered to buy bargains?

Worksheet 20.4

Practice Questions

1. Clayton purchased a new pair of pants for $17.73. He paid for it with a twenty-dollar bill. What is the correct change and how will James count it back to Clayton?

2. Isabella bought dinner for $22.12 and paid for it with a fifty-dollar bill. What is the correct change and how will Madeline count it back to Isabella?

3. What are two profitable sources of revenue for restaurants?

4. Using the quick method, estimate the temperature in Fahrenheit if it is 10°C.

5. Now compute the exact Fahrenheit equivalent of 10° Celsius.

6. You need to drive 500 kilometers today. How many miles is this? Estimate with the unit multiplier ratios.

7. Check your answer with a precise conversion on your phone or computer.

Bible and discussion questions

8. Have you ever prayed for your pastor or looked for ways to support and encourage him? Is it Biblical to do so? What is one verse which supports your answer?

9. In the third set of 10 passages, choose one which you liked the best and write it out please.

10. What are some great places your grandparents have discovered to buy bargains?

Worksheet 21.1

PRACTICE QUESTIONS

1. Why did Steve feel the need to make significant changes to his diet?

2. If he weighed 282 pounds when he began the diet, how many pounds did he lose?

3. What is a calorie?

4. Which meal has the most calories: a cola, a McDonald's quarter pounder and a large order of fries with a cookie, or a chipotle chicken salad bowl?

5. Which meal in #4 is the healthiest, in your opinion?

6. Describe Daniel's nutritional situation in Daniel 1:8-16.

7. What was the result of the experiment with veggies and water versus tasty delicacies?

Bible and Discussion Questions

8. Why does giving follow redemption?

9. What does Steve normally do when he is depressed?

10. What was your chief takeaway from this lesson?

Worksheet 21.2

Practice Questions

1. What foods did Steve eat while on the diet protocol?

2. What kind of foods did he avoid?

3. How many calories are in a pound of fat?

4. Which meal has the most calories: a Chick-fil-A Cobb salad and eight-piece grilled nuggets or a BK whopper with a cola and fries?

5. Which meal in #4 is the healthiest, in your opinion?

6. What percent of the original Cheerios is sugar?

7. What advice does Paul give to the Romans who had different opinions on what food to eat?

Bible and Discussion Questions

8. Why should you not put off giving just because you only have a little bit of money?

9. What did Steve do in 2012 that led to God giving him a remarkable illumination?

10. Are your folks label readers when they grocery shop?

Worksheet 21.3

Practice Questions

1. How many calories are recommended for men and women to ingest each day?

2. What is the oversimplified theory for losing a pound in seven days?

3. Why is this simple approach in #2 not accurate?

4. What are some other products that have the same risks as refined sugar?

5. How many calories are in a breakfast of one banana, one cup of oatmeal, a slice of toast with butter, and a 4 oz. glass of orange juice?

6. Design a healthy breakfast that will be less than 600 calories.

7. How old do you have to be for the BMI ratio and charts to be applicable?

Bible and Discussion Questions

8. When do many nonprofit ministries receive 40% or more of their donations? What does Steve suggest?

9. What did Steve do to test this wonderful picture of Jesus in the clouds?

10. What is your favorite fast-food restaurant? How many calories do you typically consume while eating there? (Do some research to discover this information.)

Worksheet 21.4

Practice Questions

1. What is BMI? What is the formula for calculating a person's BMI?

2. What is metabolism?

3. What is the missing ingredient to successful lifestyle changes?

4. Why is the fructose sugar in an apple better than a similar amount of sugar in a soda?

5. How many calories are in a meal with spaghetti, spaghetti sauce, two tablespoons of parmesan cheese, a half cup of corn, a half cup of green beans, with cake and frosting for dessert? How much would this same meal be without the cake and frosting?

6. What two factors should be present in a successful diet program?

7. Design a snack that is healthy and less than 400 calories.

Bible and Discussion Questions

8. Where are two good sources of information to learn more about a charity before giving?

9. What is "baggage" in this lesson? What affect does it have on us?

10. What advice do your parents have about weight issues?

Worksheet 22.1

Practice Questions

1. How much water should a 150-pound person consume each day? How many full 16-ounce bottles is this?

2. What kind of food is approximately 80% water?

3. How do you find your heart rate without an electronic monitor? What is your heart rate?

4. What is better than no exercise? What are three benefits of exercising?

5. How many calories will you burn by walking for 20 minutes a day?

6. Why should healthy eating and exercising be done together?

7. Approximately how many pounds of muscle does a 140-pound, healthy 18-year-old man have?

Bible and Discussion Questions

8. What is the act of grace which Paul speaks of in 2 Corinthians 8?

9. What issue from Steve's childhood continues to impact his relationship with his Heavenly Father?

10. What kind of regular exercise does your family enjoy?

Worksheet 22.2

Practice Questions

1. How much water should a 125-pound person consume each day? How many full 16-ounce bottles is this?

2. How much water is there in an apple that weighs five ounces?

3. How do you find your maximum heart rate?

4. Is it a good idea to drink water before you eat? Why?

5. How many calories will you burn by running for 15 minutes a day?

6. Enter your personal information in the Body Weight Planner at https://www.niddk.nih.gov/bwp. Was the helpful? Why?

7. How many calories does a pound of muscle burn simply maintaining itself?

Bible and Discussion Questions

8. Please summarize 2 Corinthians 9:6-8.

9. What three verses does Steve cling to for encouragement that God is always with him?

10. Do you prefer to exercise by yourself or with other people?

Worksheet 22.3

Practice Questions

1. How much water should a 184-pound person consume each day? How many full 16-ounce bottles is this?

2. How much water is there in 12 ounces of watermelon? Round the answer to a whole number.

3. What is the heart rate target zone of a 40-year-old?

4. What would be the 40-year-old's approximate bpm be if they were engaged in a high intensity workout?

5. How many calories will you burn by rowing for 25 minutes a day?

6. How many calories can a 160-pound person burn while swimming at a fast pace for 25 minutes?

7. Give two reasons why Steve enjoys working out with a group led by a coach.

Bible and Discussion Questions

8. What is the background for the promise in Philippians 4:19?

9. Write out the last three sentences of the promise to Joshua.

10. What is “temple maintenance?”

Worksheet 22.4

22.4

PRACTICE QUESTIONS

1. How much water should a 110-pound person consume each day? How many 16-ounce full bottles is this?

2. Besides the water and sugar content, what is another benefit of snacking on fruit when you are hungry?

3. When should you begin consuming water each day?

4. How many calories will you burn by jumping rope for 12 minutes a day?

5. What are three more benefits of exercising not mentioned in 22-1?

6. What is one advantage of rowing over running?

7. What is the number one piece of information you have learned in this lesson which you want to begin doing right away?

Bible and Discussion Questions

8. Which church was a giving church and how do we know?

9. What does Immanuel mean?

10. What kinds of exercise have your parents done in the past? Which ones might they recommend to you?

Worksheet 23.1

Practice Questions

1. When did fire insurance become necessary in London?

2. Name three kinds of insurance.

3. Give two examples of a catastrophic event.

4. What percentage of homes have a serious fire each year?

5. What kind of automobile insurance is required by law?

6. Why didn't Steve purchase collision coverage for his first car?

7. If you are ultimately counting on God for protection, why carry insurance?

Bible and Discussion Questions

8. Describe God's blessing in your own words.

9. How does Steve read scripture to help make it real to him?

10. Why did your folks choose their current insurance agent or agency to handle their insurance needs?

Worksheet 23.2

Practice Questions

1. When was the first volunteer fire department formed in Philadelphia? Who assisted in that effort?

2. Which kinds of insurance will you most likely purchase in your lifetime?

3. Why are premiums higher if the deductible is lower?

4. How much was the deductible for a member of the Smartphone Owners?

5. What was the annual premium for a member of the Homeowners Group who chose the $250.00 deductible?

6. What are the two components of permanent, or whole life, insurance?

7. What is term life insurance?

Bible and Discussion Questions

8. When did Jesus encourage us to pray for our daily bread? Why is that a good idea?

9. What is one way to learn more about God?

10. Do your parents or grandparents have their auto and homeowner's policies with the same agent? Do they receive a discount for doing so?

Worksheet 23.3

Practice Questions

1. Name three principles that The Philadelphia Contributionship advocated that are still present in modern insurance.

2. What is a premium? How often are they normally paid?

3. What were the monthly and annual costs of the premiums for the Smartphone Owners?

4. Seth is a member of the Smartphone Owners and breaks his screen. The cost to have the phone screen repaired is $149.00. How much will Seth have to pay? How much will the Smartphone Owners group contribute?

5. A member of the Homeowners Group submits a claim for $2,769.00 for flood damage to their home. They are in Tier 500. How much will they pay out of their own pocket and how much will the group contribute?

6. Who are the beneficiaries on a life insurance policy?

7. How is whole life insurance different from term insurance?

Bible and Discussion Questions

8. How did the blessing of God tangibly impact the children of Israel while they were in the wilderness for forty years?

9. What is another fruit of reading selected passages about what Jesus has done for us?

10. How much deductible do your folks or grandparents carry on their home?

Worksheet 23.4

Practice Questions

1. Why does this lesson on insurance also speak about assurance?

2. What is a deductible?

3. What kind of deductible should you carry on your home, high or low? Why?

4. In addition to the premium costs, what other requirements did each member of the Smartphone Owners agree to? Why did they require these?

5. What was the occupation of Matthew in the Homeowners Group? Why did they need his services?

6. How is renting a home similar to term insurance?

7. David pays $475 per year for a 10-year term life policy worth $500,000.00. How much will he have paid after making annual payments for 10 years?

Bible and Discussion Questions

8. What did Hudson Taylor mean when he said, "God's work done in God's way will never lack God's supply"?

9. What three passages touched your heart as you read them?

10. What do your parents think about deductibles? Do they have deductibles on their vehicles?

Worksheet 23.5

Practice Questions

1. What are two definitions of the word pool in the insurance world?

2. What is a cash reserve?

3. Anna is one of the first members of the Smartphone Owners. She is running through her neighborhood when she drops her phone, cracking the screen. Her phone is unusable. What are the next few steps she needs to take to have her phone repaired?

4. Faith's home needs a small repair for squirrel damage in her attic. It will cost $245.00 to fix it. She is in Tier 250. How much will she pay? How much will the Homeowners pay?

5. If David were to die after making insurance payments for three years towards his 10-year term life policy that is worth $500,000.00, how much would his beneficiaries receive?

6. Why are life insurance premiums lower for a young student than for an old teacher?

7. What is the balance that Steve advocates between being prudent and trusting God?

Bible and Discussion Questions

8. What is the temptation described in Deuteronomy 8:10–14?

9. Which verse blessed you that was new to you?

10. What do your parents think about life insurance?

Worksheet 24.1

Practice Questions

1. What is a PPO? What is one advantage of a PPO? What percentage of health plans are PPOs?

2. What is coinsurance?

3. What do the numbers mean in an 80/20 coinsurance?

4. How much would Steve contribute from each paycheck if he was in the PPO 2000 plan for 2018?

5. What is a Christian sharing plan?

6. Name three sharing companies.

7. How many people are members of BCBSA?

Bible and Discussion Questions

8. Make a list of five things for which you are thankful. Then give thanks to your Heavenly Father.

9. 9. Why is the cross a symbol for the Christian faith?

10. What kind of health insurance does your family carry?

Worksheet 24.2

Practice Questions

1. What is an HMO? What is one advantage of an HMO? What percentage of health plans are HMOs?

2. What is a PCP? What is the role of a PCP in an HMO?

3. How much did Demme Learning contribute annually for single employees in the PPO 2000 health plan in 2018?

4. What was the insurance company's responsibility on PPO 2000 plan for the "Episode?"

5. What are at least three requirements of Christian sharing plans?

6. How does a sharing plan work?

7. Where is the hope and confidence of the follower of Jesus?

Bible and Discussion Questions

8. What are your thoughts about the ten lepers who were healed?

9. If you had to choose one passage about the centrality of the cross in the good news, which one would it be? Why?

10. What are your parents' thoughts about Christian Sharing plans?

Worksheet 24.3

Practice Questions

1. What is a copay? What is self-pay?

2. What does it mean for a provider to be "in network?" What is the advantage of choosing a specialist in network?

3. How much were Steve's out of pocket expenses for the Episode?

4. How much did the insurance company pay for the Episode?

5. If there is a plan entitled PPO 3500, what might the number represent?

6. How was the submitted claim shared by the members of Samaritan Ministries?

7. What is a catastrophic need?

Bible and Discussion Questions

8. Where does every good and perfect gift come from?

9. What does it mean to die daily and take up your cross daily?

10. Does your parents' healthcare plan come through their place of work?

Worksheet 24.4

Practice Questions

1. What is a deductible in a health plan? What was the amount of the deductible in the Demme Learning plan?

2. What does it mean to be out of network?

3. What is an adjustment and why did Steve receive it in the Episode, Part 2?

4. How did the adjustment impact Steve's bill for the Episode, Part 2?

5. What percentage of the total bill was subtracted as adjustments under the sharing plan?

6. How much does Steve pay to Samaritan Ministries beyond his monthly share for catastrophic coverage?

7. Why do some people go bankrupt when they are out of work for a few months?

Bible and Discussion Questions

8. What can you do to foster a grateful heart and be thankful?

9. Write out your favorite promise found in the verses in the section on being "United with Christ."

10. Is your parents' insurance plan a PPO or HMO? Are they happy with their coverage and costs?

Worksheet 24.5

Practice Questions

1. What is a formal definition of insurance?

2. What is an insurance policy?

3. What would Steve's coinsurance portion have been for a $11,115.56 bill if his plan had been 70/30 out-of-network coinsurance after deductible, if he had used his deductible, if the insurance company did not adjust the costs, and if he was out of network?

4. What would the insurance company's responsibility have been for a $11,115.56 bill if his plan had been 70/30 out-of-network coinsurance after deductible, if he had used his deductible, if the insurance company did not adjust the costs, and if he was out of network?

5. What is a spiritual/emotional cause of physical sickness?

6. What two guidelines would Steve add to the sharing guidelines if he had the opportunity?

7. What is a prudent way to prepare for unexpected medical emergencies?

Bible and Discussion Questions

8. When was the last time you thanked your parents for something that is easy to take for granted, like preparing meals or working to provide for a home and clothes? Your assignment is to thank each of them for one thing. The more specific the better!

9. How do the sacraments of the communion and baptism remind us of the cross?

10. What kind of health coverage do your grandparents have? What are their thoughts about their healthcare?

Worksheet 25.1

Practice Questions

1. What does it mean to count the cost of a college education?

2. Why is Harrisburg Area Community College (HACC) called a commuter school?

3. What is the difference between a grant/scholarship and a loan?

4. If there are five classes in each semester, what is the tuition cost for each class for an in state student at Millersville University?

5. How much does it cost to attend Millersville University for four years and live on campus?

6. If you attended HACC for two years, and then transferred to Millersville and completed your degree program in two more years, how much did you save instead of going to MU all four years?

7. If you passed CLEP exams for four semester classes at Millersville, how much did you save?

Bible and Discussion Questions

8. What are two reasons to keep the Sabbath holy?

9. What set of words helps Steve understand justification?

10. What do your parents think about you attending a two-year or four-year college? What do they perceive as the pluses and minuses of college for you?

Worksheet 25.2

PRACTICE QUESTIONS

1. What are two kinds of loans available to help finance a college education?

2. What is an FAFSA? Who needs to complete this application?

3. What percent of students attending Lancaster Bible College receive some form of financial aid?

For numbers 4-7: Clayton believes God is leading him to attend Lancaster Bible College and live on campus. He applies for and receives $15,000 in financial aid. Since he works at Chick-fil-A, he filled out the application for a scholarship and received $3,500 from his employer.

4. How much does Clayton need to borrow from the government for his freshman and sophomore years?

5. For his junior and senior years, Clayton heard about an opportunity to live off campus with a friend of the family, so he would not have to pay for housing. He did commit to paying the family $75 per week (36 weeks of school) for food. How much did he save each year he lived there?

6. How much did he have to borrow his last two years of school?

7. What would Clayton's total student debt be if he maintained a high grade-point average and received the same financial aid and scholarship each year he was at school?

Bible and Discussion Questions

8. What is one benefit of setting aside one day for rest?

9. How does the Passover foreshadow and teach us about Jesus?

10. What advice do your folks have about financing postsecondary educational options?

Worksheet 25.3

Practice Questions

1. What is a merit-based scholarship?

2. Name at least two organizations that may offer scholarships.

3. What do the letters EFC represent?

For numbers 4-7: Miriam graduated from college with a student loan debt of $27,500 at 6.25% interest for 10 years.

4. How much is her monthly payment?

5. How much interest will she pay?

6. How much could she save (in time and interest) by adding $35 to each monthly payment?

7. Miriam's job is paying her $49,800 per year, and she will pay 21% in taxes. What is her net income? What percentage of her monthly net income will her student loan payment be?

Bible and Discussion Questions

8. What can we do on the Sabbath that is beneficial?

9. What is the difference between the Old Testament sacrifices of animals and the sacrifice of Jesus in Hebrews 9:13–14?

10. What does your family think about graduating from college with a large debt?

Worksheet 25.4

Practice Questions

1. What is a CLEP test?

2. How do CELP exams save you money?

3. If you decide to take a CELP exam, how many subjects are you able to choose from?

For numbers 4-7: Drew graduated from college with a significant student loan to pay back. He borrowed $38,000 at 5.5% interest for 15 years.

4. How much is his monthly payment?

5. How much interest will he pay?

6. How much could he save (in time and interest) by adding $25 to each monthly payment?

7. If Drew's job is paying him $56,500 per year, and he will pay 22% in taxes, what is his net income? What percentage of his monthly net income will his student loan payment be?

Bible and Discussion Questions

8. What two things does Steve think Paul directs believers to do in Romans 14?

9. Why was the curtain being torn in two when Jesus perished on the cross, so significant to us today?

10. Do you parents or grandparents know about any scholarships or grants you could apply for to offset some of the expenses for attending college?

Worksheet 25.5

PRACTICE QUESTIONS

1. What is need-based gift aid?

2. What are some pros and cons of taking a CLEP exam independently?

3. What will help you secure a private loan from a bank or credit union?

For numbers 4-7: Abigail would like to earn a two year architectural technology degree. She applies and is accepted to Thaddeus Stevens College of Technology. She sharpens her pencil and begins to see how she can save money for her degree.

4. In looking over the curriculum, she sees two math courses and one English course she thinks she can get credit for by taking a CLEP exam. If tuition is $4,000 for 5 classes, how much does she save the first year?

5. Her aunt and uncle live in Lancaster, and are walking distance from the bus route, so she can live with them and not need a car. How much will this save her if she pays them $50 per week for food (36 weeks)?

6. She applies for four scholarships and receives two for $1,000 each. She also completes the FAFSA application and receives $3,500 in financial aid. How much will she need to borrow for her degree?

7. While she is applying to the government for a student loan, her grandparents call and tell her that God is leading them to send a check to her of $5,000 towards her education. After giving thanks for this wonderful gift, how much does she owe now?

BIBLE AND DISCUSSION QUESTIONS

8. Which passage was especially meaningful to you in this study on the Sabbath?

9. What are two benefits of celebrating the Lord's Supper?

10. Interview your older siblings (if you have some) or other friends who are either in college or recently graduated from college about how they financed their education.

Worksheet 26.1

PRACTICE QUESTIONS

1. In what field of study did Steve receive his undergraduate degree?

2. After reading "The Cross and the Switchblade" how did his life plans change?

3. What is hindsight? How would Steve have proceeded if he had known all the current options for post high school education?

4. What did Steve's three sons do after they graduated from home education?

5. What are some benefits of going to college when you are older?

6. Who knows the best plan for you when you graduate and begin thinking about how to prepare for your future?

7. What is the essence of Proverbs 11:14? How can you apply this concept in your life?

Bible and Discussion Questions

8. What is the message of the wise men and the foolish men in the Sermon on the Mount?

9. How does Jesus respond when we weep?

10. What did your parents do the first year after they completed high school?

Worksheet 26.2

Practice Questions

1. What are two positive aspects of attending a Christian institution?

2. What are two areas of concern when attending a Christian institution?

3. What are two positive aspects of attending a secular institution?

4. What does Steve believe is essential when being a part of a secular environment?

5. Do a little research and see which of these student ministries looks like a good fit for you. See if they are at the school you may be attending.

6. What is the three-point mission of CCO? (By the way, I almost worked with this ministry when I completed college.)

7. What are two areas of concern if you attend a secular institution?

Bible and Discussion Questions

8. How is being just and fair an extension of our faith?

9. How does Isaiah 53 describe and reveal Jesus?

10. What do your parents think you are best suited to do after high school?

Worksheet 26.3

Practice Questions

1. What are two factors which are changing the way we look at post high school education alternatives?

2. One-third of which occupations are predicted to make up all new jobs between 2019 and 2033?

3. What percentage of construction companies are having trouble hiring people to fill their open positions?

4. What is an apprentice?

5. Why is being an apprentice a win-win scenario for the student and the employer?

6. If you could choose one occupation to pursue for three to six months as an apprentice, which one would it be?

7. What is a "gap year"?

Bible and Discussion Questions

8. What is restitution? How did Steve apply it in his new life as a believer?

9. What are the qualifications for being a leader in God's Kingdom?

10. With 20–20 hindsight, what do your parents wish they had done after graduating from high school?

Worksheet 26.4

PRACTICE QUESTIONS

1. What are the costs of OneLife for one year? What does that expense cover?

2. What are some of the advantages of a gap year?

3. Are you able to receive scholarships if you enroll in a gap year program?

4. What is a career assessment tool?

5. Visit the page on https://www.crown.org/career/#my-investment, and list two benefits of taking the Career Direct Assessment. What is the most popular option which people choose?

6. What is one good fruit that comes from evaluating how God has wired you?

7. What is HSLDA? How did they begin?

Bible and Discussion Questions

8. Why was Isaac Newton chosen to to be Master of the Royal Mint?

9. How did Jesus give an example to His disciple that they were to serve one another?

10. What does your family think about a gap year or an apprenticeship?

Worksheet 27.1

Practice Questions

1. What is a resume?

2. What are hard skills?

3. Are you an extrovert or an introvert, outgoing or reserved?

4. What does it mean to have a blend of personality "types"?

5. Who was the grandmother of David? Which nation was she from?

6. Who spent most of their life in politics in a foreign kingdom?

7. How did being a shepherd prepare a few of the men in scripture to be in leadership positions?

Bible and discussion questions

8. Why does Benny want me to co-sign a loan with him? Is this a good idea?

9. Who receives grace from God? Which passage supports this idea?

10. What do your parents and grandparents think are your soft skills?

Worksheet 27.2

Practice Questions

1. What are four examples of soft skills?

2. What is the difference between hard and soft skills?

3. After taking the personality assessment, which one of the four personality types do you think best describes you?

4. According to the page on this personality type, what are some of your strengths and weaknesses?

5. Which two men used their gifts to create the holy articles found in the temple of Israel?

6. What were the occupations of the two brothers and their cousin described in Genesis?

7. What kind of personality do you think Simon Peter the apostle exemplifies?

Bible and Discussion Questions

8. The Spirit of God authored Scripture. What is the meaning of this graphic picture in Proverbs 6? "Now swallow your pride; go and beg to have your name erased. Don't put it off; do it now! Don't rest until you do. Save yourself like a gazelle escaping from a hunter, like a bird fleeing from a net."

9. What is the antithesis of humility? Who has it?

10. Ask your parents about their favorite job or jobs. Why did they like that particular job(s)?

Worksheet 27.3

Practice Questions

1. Write out your resume at this stage in your life. Include hard and soft skills.

2. Why is home education effective in preparing students for the real world?

3. What kind of personality does Jesus have?

4. What does it mean say that someone has a blend of personality traits?

5. Who worked side by side with Paul making and repairing tents?

6. Who was Prime Minister after serving as Prison Minister?

7. Which occupation in Scripture do you think you were designed to do?

Bible and Discussion Questions

8. When might co-signing be a good idea?

9. What character quality did Jesus and Moses have in common?

10. Ask your grandparents about their favorite job or jobs. Why did they like that particular job(s)?

Worksheet 27.4

Practice Questions

1. What is one advantage to being home educated?

2. What is a reference? Who are two people that could provide a reference for you?

3. Which personality likes to be in charge?

4. Which personality is careful about being accurate? Which animal is associated with this type?

5. Which wealthy ladies supported Jesus and the disciples?

6. What are three reasons for working found in Scripture?

7. Which occupation in the Bible looks most interesting to you?

Bible and Discussion Questions

8. What advice does Steve have for people who are entering into a lending relationship with their family or friends?

9. How do we become the greatest members of God's kingdom?

10. What were the occupations your folks liked the least? How did God bring good from them?

Worksheet 28.1

Practice Questions

1. What is a competitive edge or advantage?

2. What competitive advantage(s) do you have?

3. What are the characteristics of an entrepreneur?

4. Why are many entrepreneurs first born children with high "D" or lion personality traits?

5. What struck you about the two shoe salesmen? What was different about their reports to headquarters about what they had found?

6. Do you have any ideas for starting your own business? If so, what are they?

7. In a business, how can a beaver help and complement an otter?

Bible and Discussion Questions

8. What does it mean to you, to be yoked with Jesus?

9. What is the first and greatest commandment?

10. What are your parents's thoughts about the pluses and minuses of being an employee or employer as an occupation?

Worksheet 28.2

Practice Questions

1. What were some of Steve's advantages when painting?

2. What is in your hand?

3. What was in the hand of Moses? What was he able to accomplish with God's help?

4. What experience did Steve have which prepared him for cutting grass and shoveling snow for his neighbors?

5. What needs did Steve observe which led to his painting people's homes?

6. What are some needs that you can meet, and be paid for doing so?

7. If you were in charge of a business who would you put in charge of the shipping department, a golden retriever or a lion? Why? Do you have any other thoughts about this situation?

Bible and Discussion Questions

8. How does 2 Corinthians 6:14-18 help you think about a potential business partnership?

9. Where does "Love your neighbor as yourself" first appear in Scripture? Did this location surprise you?

10. What are your grandparents's thoughts about being the pluses and minuses of being an employee or employer as an occupation?

Worksheet 28.3

Practice Questions

1. Why should your business be profitable?

2. What aspects of selling sno-cones did Steve enjoy? Why didn't he continue selling sno-cones?

3. What experiences have you had, which have prepared you for working in a business?

4. If you are thinking about getting started having your own business, what are two things Steve recommends you can do to begin?

5. Whom do you know that operates their own business? Could you interview them?

6. What do you think would be three great questions to ask an entrepreneur?

7. If you needed two people to work together and give an interesting and informative presentation, who would you pick to be with the beaver?

Bible and Discussion Questions

8. How does 2 Corinthians 6:14-18 apply to a possible marriage relationship?

9. What is the new commandment? Where does this new way of loving others appear in the gospel of John?

10. There is an Amish saying, "Too soon old. Too late smart." What advice would your parents and grandparents have for you based on their years of experience as an employer or an employee?

Worksheet 28.4

Practice Questions

1. Which needs did Steve meet with his math program?

2. Which principles governed the way he conducted His business?

3. Name two businesses that began with a few guys sitting around a table brainstorming.

4. What did you learn from the story of the invention of the Braille alphabet?

5. How did Wiffle Ball come about?

6. What prompted the Demmes to have an herbal business in their basement?

7. Your firm is looking for someone to hire who is patient and steady to help with the customer service department. Which personality trait would you be looking for? Why?

BIBLE AND DISCUSSION QUESTIONS

8. What does Steve recommend when considering a close working relationship with a believer?

9. How did Paul apply the new commandment to his instructions to husbands in Ephesians 5:25?

10. If your parents had one piece of advice to share with you about entering the work arena, what would it be?

Worksheet 29.1

Practice Questions

1. Why does Steve think we all work for somebody?

2. Who was a part of Steve's team when he first began MathUSee?

3. Who joined MathUSee and made it into the company it is today?

4. What are some of the responsibilities of an employee?

5. What are some of the responsibilities of an employer?

6. Describe Steve's typical work day as a painting contractor.

7. Describe a typical day for one of Steve's painters.

Bible and Discussion Questions

8. What is one negative result, or fruit, of lotteries and gambling?

9. Why was Steve unable to be still and wait on God?

10. Who was each of your parents' favorite employer? Why?

Worksheet 29.2

Practice Questions

1. What were the potential risks and rewards for a painting contractor?

2. What are three pluses of being self-employed that appeal to you?

3. What are three minuses of being self-employed that make you a little concerned?

4. What are some of the benefits of being an employee from your perspective?

5. What do the words “feast and famine” mean for someone who is self-employed?

6. What jobs are you aware of that fit your passions and how God designed you?

7. What lessons have you learned from difficult work experiences or responsibilities?

Bible and Discussion Questions

8. What advice would you give to someone who asks what is wrong with getting rich quickly?

9. Why does Steve refer to God as a gentleman?

10. What kind of occupation or job situation do your folks think would be a good fit for you?

Worksheet 29.3

Practice Questions

1. What does it mean to have long hours as an employer?

2. What are three pluses of being an employee that appeal to you?

3. What are three minuses of being an employee that cause you concern?

4. Would you rather be an employee or an employer? Why?

5. Explain how a person's personality influences whether they tend to be self-employed or employed.

6. How was David prepared to be a king?

7. How was Moses prepared to lead the children of Israel through the wilderness?

Bible and Discussion Questions

8. Why are there really no winners in a lottery or gambling activity, just losers?

9. Have you set aside a specific time to be still and wait on God?

10. Who was your grandparents' favorite employer? Why?

Worksheet 29.4

Practice Questions

1. What does the expression mean, "the boss sets the tone?"

2. What lessons did Steve learn while teaching in a classroom?

3. What are the advantages of tutoring over classroom teaching?

4. What part of the section on "Providence of God" stood out to you?

5. How did MathUSee begin?

6. What does Steve look for when hiring employees and co-workers?

7. What was the difference between the friend who became a Marine and the son of a painter?

Bible and Discussion Questions

8. If you had a billboard, which one of the verses under "Great Advice" would you place near a major roadway? Why?

9. What does Psalm 34:8 mean to you?

10. What kind of occupation or job situation do your grandparents' think would be a great fit for you?

Worksheet 30.1

Practice Questions

1. Find the simple interest on a one-year investment with a principal of $500.00 at 6%.

2. Find the interest on a one-year investment with a principal of $500.00 at 6%, compounded quarterly. Find the solution by working through the calculations in a table.

3. Compute the compound interest on a one-year investment with a principal of $500.00 at 6%, compounded continuously by using the Stewardship Investment Calculator. How much is the final value of your investment after one year?

4. If you had your money in a simple interest account, what would the interest rate have to be to give you the same return on your money as the compound interest account in #3?

5. Which will produce the greatest return on your $400.00 CD, a 6.5% interest rate compounded annually for two years, or a 6% interest rate compounded quarterly for two years? Use the formula for computing compound interest.

6. Check your work in #5 by using the investment calculator.

7. What is the difference between simple and compound interest?

Bible and Discussion Questions

8. In the first section under "Standing before Kings" there are eight Proverbs listed. Which one is the most encouraging to you? Why?

9. Why does Steve continue to read and reread portions of Psalm 139?

10. When did your parents first learn about the difference between simple and compound interest?

Worksheet 30.2

Practice Questions

1. Find the simple interest on a one-year investment with a principal of $800.00 at 12%.

2. Find the interest on a one-year investment with a principal of $800.00 at 12%, compounded quarterly. Find the solution by working through the calculations in a table.

3. Compute the compound interest on a one-year investment with a principal of $800.00 at 12%, compounded continuously by using the Stewardship Investment Calculator. How much is the final value of your investment after one year?

4. If you had your money in a simple interest account, what would the interest rate have to be to give you the same return on your money as the compound interest account in #3?

5. How much interest will be generated by a $250.00 CD with a 4% interest rate compounded monthly for three years? Use the formula for computing compound interest and round to ten-thousandths as you are calculating.

6. What does it mean when the interest is compounded annually?

7. Using the Stewardship Investment Calculator, find the final value of a CD with a principal of $375.00 and a rate of interest of 5.25% compounded weekly for five years.

BIBLE AND DISCUSSION QUESTIONS

8. In the first section under "Standing before Kings" there are eight Proverbs listed. Which one is the most convicting to you? Why?

9. What is your favorite passage(s) in Psalm 139 and why?

10. How has compound interest helped your family?

Worksheet 30.3

30.3

Practice Questions

1. Find the simple interest on a three-year investment with a principal of $10,000.00 at 5% annual interest note.

2. Now compute the interest on a three-year investment with a principal of 10,000.00 at 5% compounded annually. Find the solution by working through the calculations in a table.

3. Calculate the compound interest on a three-year investment with a principal of $10,000.00 at 5% compounded monthly by using the Stewardship Investment Calculator. How much is the final value of your investment after three years?

4. If you had the same amount of money in an account collecting only simple interest, what would the yearly interest rate have to be to produce the same return as in #3?

5. Which produces the best return on a $1,000.00 CD, a 4 1/2% interest rate compounded annually for six years, or a 3 3/4% interest rate compounded monthly for six years? Use a calculator.

6. What is the principal?

7. Using the Stewardship Investment Calculator, find the final value of a CD with a principal of $850.00 and a rate of interest of 4 1/4% compounded monthly for eight years.

BIBLE AND DISCUSSION QUESTIONS

8. How did Steve learn to meet God half way?

9. With which of these temptations in the Scripture Studies do you most identify?

10. How can the principle of compounding interest become a burden to your family?

Worksheet 30.4

Practice Questions

1. Find the simple interest on a four-year investment with a principal of $2,500.00 at 8%.

2. Now compute the compound interest on a four-year investment with a principal of $2,500.00 at 8% compounded annually. Find the solution by working through the calculations in a table.

3. Calculate the compound interest on a four-year investment with a principal of $2,500.00 at 8% compounded monthly by using the Stewardship Investment Calculator. How much is the final value of your investment after four years?

4. If you had the same amount of money in an account collecting only simple interest, what would the yearly interest rate have to be to produce the same return as in #3?

5. How much interest will be generated by a $3,000.00 CD with a 3.5% interest rate compounded monthly for 48 months?

6. How many months in a quarter?

7. Using the Stewardship Investment Calculator, find the final value of a CD that has a principal of $1,500.00 and a rate of interest of 2.5% compounded quarterly for eight years.

BIBLE AND DISCUSSION QUESTIONS

8. What is character and why do you think it is important?

9. Which of the truth antidotes are the most encouraging to you?

10. What advice do your parents have on the best way to harness the power of compound interest?

Worksheet 31.1

Practice Questions

1. What is surplus?

2. What is speculation and why is it risky?

3. Which adjectives does Steve use to describe the kind of investing he endorses?

4. What is price inflation?

5. You begin investing $100.00 per month from age 18 until you are 48 (30 years). How much total money did you contribute to the principal through these monthly contributions? If your annual rate of return is 5% compounded monthly before each investment, what is the total value of your investment after 30 years? Please use the online investment calculator.

6. You begin investing $240.00 per month from age 25 until you are 40 (15 years). How much total money did you contribute to the principal through these monthly contributions? If your annual rate of return is 5% compounded monthly before each investment, what is the total value of your investment after 15 years? Please use the online investment calculator.

7. Which is the wisest course, beginning at a young age as in #5, or starting to save when you are older as in #6?

Bible and Discussion Questions

8. What are some of the benefits of working with your hands?

9. What is the work of God?

10. Have your parents ever been asked to be involved in a get rich quickly speculation? Ask them details if they are comfortable sharing about it. What did they learn?

Worksheet 31.2

PRACTICE QUESTIONS

1. What have you learned from the illustration of the $100.00 in the shoe box and the price of a gallon of milk?

2. What the average annual rate of inflation over the past 30 years?

3. The message of the tortoise, hare, and woodchuck is clear, start early and stick to it. How much could you save in a month if you began right now?

4. What is the best kind of exercise and the best kind of investment?

5. You begin investing $75.00 per month from age 25 until you are 58 (33 years). How much total money did you contribute to the principal through these monthly contributions? If your annual rate of return is 6% compounded monthly before each investment, what is the total value of your investment after 33 years?

6. You begin investing $150.00 per month from age 40 until you are 65 (25 years). How much total money did you contribute to the principal through these monthly contributions? If your annual rate of return is 6% compounded monthly before each investment, what is the total value of your investment after 25 years?

7. Which investment strategy yield the highest return, #5, or #6? Why?

Bible and Discussion Questions

8. What positive fruit followed Paul's work as a tentmaker?

9. Define faith in your own words.

10. What kinds of investments have worked best for your parents? What advice do they have about diversifying their savings among different kinds of investments?

Worksheet 31.3

Practice Questions

1. What is APR and which kind of interest is it similar to, simple or compound?

2. What is APY and which kind of interest is it similar to, simple or compound?

3. Write out the formula for converting APR to APY using words.

4. If your $600.00 investment is growing at a rate of 9% interest, how many years will it take to double in value?

5. Find the interest on a two-year investment with a principal of $1,500.00 at 12%, compounded annually.

6. Find the compound interest on a two-year investment with a principal of $1,500.00 at 12%, compounded quarterly.

7. Compute the compound interest on a two-year investment with a principal of 1,500.00 at 12%, compounded monthly. You may write your conclusions without making a table. You can either use a scientific calculator to help you with this, or you can use Excel and make a program to perform these calculations. You can also access an investment calculator created at MathUSee.com/invest.

BIBLE AND DISCUSSION QUESTIONS

8. How did Steve's work experience as a carpenter and painter help him in the ministry?

9. Why was Abraham called the father of all who believe?

10. What are your parents' thoughts about IRAs and 401Ks?

Worksheet 31.4

Practice Questions

1. What are two popular methods of determining the minimum payment on a credit card balance?

2. What is a portfolio?

3. What is free money and how is it connected to a 401K?

4. If your $1,350 investment is growing at a rate of 12% interest, how many years will it take to double in value?

5. If you had $250.00 invested in a 7.5% interest bearing savings account that is compounded monthly, what would be the value of your investment after 30 years?

6. If you had $250.00 invested in a 7.5% interest bearing savings account that is compounded continuously, how much would the original investment have grown to in 30 years? Compare the result with #5.

7. You begin investing $25.00 per month from age 20 until you are 50 (30 years). If your annual rate of return is 6.25% compounded monthly before each investment, what is the total value of your investment when you are 50?

Bible and Discussion Questions

8. What are two ways the worthy woman worked with her hands?

9. How does faith grow?

10. What items have your grandparents seen increase in price the most during their lifetime?

PRACTICE QUESTIONS

1. What is diversification and which of the four kinds of investments will you most likely have in your portfolio?

2. What is the difference between a standard or traditional IRA and a Roth IRA?

3. What kind of IRA is best suited to someone who is 23 years old and just beginning to work full-time? Why?

4. You invest $250 in a CD that pays 3% interest. How long will you have to leave it in the bank until it doubles in value?

5. The woodchuck finally begins investing for his future by contributing $400.00 per month into an account that yields 5.75% interest and is compounded monthly, when he is 40. How much principal will he have invested by the time he is 55 years old? What is the size of his nest egg?

6. The tortoise invests the same amount of principal as his woodchuck associate, but begins when he is 19 by contributing $200 per month, and faithfully continues until he is 49. How big is his nest egg?

7. What does Steve mean when he says to continue your education?

Bible and Discussion Questions

8. Who assigned Adam and Eve the task of tending and watching over the garden of Eden?

9. Which passage about faith in this study encourages you?

10. What advice do your grandparents have about investing for the future?

Worksheet 32.1

Practice Questions

1. What are the traditional three responses when a follower of Jesus hears about significant needs that touch our heart?

2. What did John Bunyan mean when he said, "You can do more than pray, after you have prayed, but you cannot do more than pray until you have prayed"?

3. What was R. G. LeTourneau's ambition when it came to giving?

4. Why does Steve think giving is a Christian virtue?

5. What percentage of United States citizens are involved in some form of charity or nonprofit enterprise?

6. Where in Scripture does Jesus encourage us to give?

7. What summer experience had a major impact on Steve when he was a young man?

Bible and Discussion Questions

8. Do you know any people who are poor, orphans, or widows? Please write down their names.

9. Explain what Steve means when he says, "Our enemies are not flesh and blood."

10. Have you and your parents engaged in praying, giving, and going?

Worksheet 32.2

Practice Questions

1. Where did Steve travel outside the U.S. to help needy children?

2. Name one lesson Steve learned while serving as chairman of this nonprofit entity formed to support those children in South India.

3. How does our giving of our time and treasure connect to our heart?

4. What is the second command that is similar to the first and great commandment?

5. What two books made a huge impact on Steve's thinking as he grew in understanding of better ways to pray, give, and go?

6. What are three words or phrases which we normally think of to describe those who are poor or who live in poverty?

7. Are the characteristics in #6 measurable? If so, which ones can be measured?

Bible and Discussion Questions

8. How is it possible to "lend to the Lord"?

9. In John 10:10 Jesus describes Himself and the devil. What is the ministry of Jesus? What is the mission of the devil?

10. What outreaches does your church or community have for supporting those who are poor and live in a state of poverty?

Worksheet 32.3

Practice Questions

1. Give three words or phrases that some of the 60,000 poor individuals interviewed used to express how they viewed their plight.

2. What other words from *Voices of the Poor* were windows into the heart of how these people felt and perceived themselves?

3. What is the difference between poverty of being and a serious lack of material needs?

4. What is the most difficult sin that lies deep in each of our hearts?

5. Can you quote or talk about a phrase in the section by C. S. Lewis about pride that made an impression on you?

6. How do the givers and the receivers both suffer when traditional charity is being practiced?

7. Why does Steve feel rich by every metric?

Bible and Discussion Questions

8. What is "religion that is pure and undefiled before God"?

9. What did Steve witness first hand at Yad Vashem?

10. What do your parents think about the warfare we are engaged in as Christians?

Worksheet 32.4

Practice Questions

1. What does Steve think is a blind spot shared by followers of Jesus who live in the affluent West?

2. What is the antidote to feeling superior?

3. How did Jesus enter our world to save us?

4. How can we be a great helper to others?

5. What does this phrase mean to you: "In humility count others more significant than yourselves"?

6. If you were a part of the Miller family from the suburbs in "The Inner-City Christmas, Part 1," how would you have felt when you distributed the gifts to the children?

7. If you were one of the Kingston children, how would you feel?

Bible and Discussion Questions

8. Have you had an opportunity to pray, give, or visit widows and/or orphans in your church or community?

9. How does Steve take action against feeling down, depressed, and hopeless?

10. Has your family ever tried to help others and it did not go as well as you hoped?

Worksheet 33.1

Practice Questions

1. Where did the desire to love our neighbor as ourselves come from?

2. What is the response of the believer to God's love for us?

3. What is the first step in seeking how to love our neighbor as ourselves?

4. Give several examples of physical poverty.

5. Describe "poverty of being."

6. When you read about the physical dimensions of poverty in the world today, which statistic surprised you the most?

7. If the population of the world in 2018 was 7.7 billion, what percentage of the world did not have adequate sanitation? Round your answer to a whole number percentage.

Bible and Discussion Questions

8. Why does the Bible counsel us to not receive bribes?

9. Which translation of "sarx" in Greek helps you understand the carnal nature the best?

10. What do your parents think about the difference between physical poverty and poverty of being?

Worksheet 33.2

Practice Questions

1. What percentage of the world lives on less than $1.25 per day? Round your answer to a whole number percentage.

2. Describe Bob Pierce in a few sentences.

3. Give an example of a short-term need.

4. How would you describe the response of the Good Samaritan: a short-term solution or a long-term strategy?

5. What are the three missing words used to describe the progression from "appreciation" to "dependency."

6. What does this sentence mean? "When we continue to provide temporary or a short time solution over a long period of time, our quick response, which was appropriate and necessary at the time of the incident, can become harmful."

7. Can you identify with the birthday illustration?

Bible and Discussion Questions

8. What were the qualifications for trustworthy people in leadership?

9. With which of the three passages describing the war within, do you most identify?

10. Which charities are well thought of by your parents? Why?

Worksheet 33.3

Practice Questions

1. What are three negative results of dependency?

2. What are the effects of dependency on the next generation who grow up watching their parent(s) receive ongoing aid?

3. How does Proverbs 14:12 apply to the giving which leads to dependency?

4. Name four words used by the poor to describe their condition.

5. Which of President Reagan's quotes did you like the most? Why?

6. Do you agree with the statement by John Perkins? Why?

7. Why did Paul forgo his right to be supported by the local church in Thessalonika?

Bible and Discussion Questions

8. How were bribes a part of the resurrection account?

9. Describe the carnal or fleshly nature.

10. What advice do your parents have about giving to a charity?

PRACTICE QUESTIONS

1. When Abraham Lincoln wrote his letter to his stepbrother, was he seeking to provide a short-term solution or an effective long-term strategy? Explain.

2. What was his advice to John Johnston?

3. How would you have felt if you had been John Johnston?

4. Would it have been easier for Mr. Lincoln to write a check or write a letter?

5. What do you predict would have been the result of a quickly written check for eighty dollars?

6. Robert Lupton was in a meeting with people discussing the food pantry. What do you think about the person's response to his question about why they still write checks?

7. Describe how to be a teachable Westerner.

Bible and Discussion Questions

8. How is God described in Deuteronomy 10:17?

9. Using your own words, describe the fruit of the Spirit in our life.

10. What do your folks think of the three quotes by President Reagan and John Perkins?

Worksheet 33.5

Practice Questions

1. What was the short-term strategy of the church in the U.S. to deal with the Rwanda genocide? Was it needed and appropriate?

2. What did you learn about Jean and his egg business?

3. What was the impact on Jean's village when the church did not shift gears between a short-term response and a long-term strategy?

4. How could the western church, which was generously giving to the Rwandans, have done a better job of helping?

5. Concerning the first model to provide water, do you understand how this could be a typical response by well-meaning American believers?

6. Which model is easier to do? Why?

7. Why is the second model for providing water a better long-term strategy?

Bible and Discussion Questions

8. Explain: “There is always free cheese in a mouse trap.”

9. Which of the words and phrases used in the Message to describe the fruits of the Spirit, help you the most?

10. Which charities are well thought of by your grandparents? Why?

Worksheet 34.1

PRACTICE QUESTIONS

1. What is the difference between a hand-up and a hand-out?

2. What is micro-finance?

3. Is there a difference between micro-finance and Christian micro-finance? Please describe the distinction.

4. How did Hope International begin?

5. How did this well-meaning organization adapt to the people's needs in the Ukraine?

6. What is micro-enterprise development?

7. Describe the organization Help the Needy and what it seeks to accomplish.

Bible and Discussion Questions

8. How did this verse impact Steve and his family? "Who swears to his own hurt and does not change." (Psalm 15:4)

9. What it is message of the wolves which the grandfather shared with his grandson?

10. Have your parents had any experience with Christian micro-finance?

Worksheet 34.2

Practice Questions

1. How would you describe Building Families of Faith?

2. Which organization, HTN or BFF is a traditional charity, and which one is a Christian micro-finance model?

3. What do you think of the Raines' idea to compare the two approaches to alleviating poverty?

4. Would you prefer to be a member of the Turner family or the Sams family? Why?

5. Which approach is the easiest to sell to the American church? Why?

6. What transpires during a savings group meeting?

7. Why do you think being a part of a Christ honoring savings group is so helpful?

Bible and Discussion Questions

8. What promise did Steve recall when thinking about the Exodus?

9. Who is on our side in our daily struggle with our old sinful nature?

10. What are your parents's thoughts about creating dependency through charitable giving?

Worksheet 34.3

Practice Questions

1. What is R.O.I.?

2. How would you measure the impact of CMF (Christian micro-finance) versus TC (traditional charity)?

3. What are overhead expenses? About how much is spent on these expenses from each donation?

4. At the end of year one, how would you compare the fruit of HTN and BFF?

5. How was the money contributed to the Johnsons spent?

6. How was the loan invested in the Sams family spent?

7. Where did the $308 come from in the BFF model? Who keeps the $8 and why?

Bible and Discussion Questions

8. How can we emulate God our Father?

9. What are some practical ways that you can sow to the Spirit?

10. What do your parents think about the difference between a hand-out and a hand-up?

Worksheet 34.4

Practice Questions

1. Why do you think Mr. Turner left his family in year three of HTN?

2. What effect does the action of Mr. Turner have on the rest of the family and the community?

3. How did the onsite coordinator now have $516 to disburse in year three?

4. How was the $516 invested?

5. Describe life in the Johnson home after receiving aid for five years.

6. Describe the ongoing dynamics of the families receiving loans and training from BFF.

7. How do the children in the CMF program benefit from their parents receiving support and loans from BFF?

Bible and Discussion Questions

8. Would you rather be poor and honest or rich and crooked? Why?

9. How do we put on humility and meekness?

10. What thoughts do your grandparents have about the idea of "teach me to fish" versus "give me a fish"?

Worksheet 34.5

Practice Questions

1. What was the impact of CMF on the local church?

2. What are some positive changes to the communities as a result of the CMF approach in BFF?

3. Were you surprised at seeing the Turner family in the BFF model in year five? Did you notice the baby?

4. What percentage of small micro loans are repaid? Does that surprise you?

5. What does it mean to have "$1,240 dollars at work on the ground in the country of Rwanda"?

6. What are your thoughts about the grades the Raines family assigned to each category?

7. Can you think of any other categories which should be added in the evaluation process?

Bible and Discussion Questions

8. What can you and I do, that God can't?

9. What does Steve have to work hard at when it comes to the battle with the wolves?

10. What additional advice do your parents and grandparents have about traditional charitable giving?

Worksheet 35.1

Practice Questions

1. What is the essence of the Great Commission in your own words?

2. Where else in the New Testament do you find similar language to Matthew 28:18-20?

3. To whom did Jesus give the command to go and make disciples; the whole church, or just a special few?

4. What is a people group?

5. How many people groups are there in the word, according to the Joshua Project?

6. How many of these groups are unreached?

7. What percent of the world's population is unreached with the gospel?

Bible and Discussion Questions

8. Is it possible to serve both God and money? Why or why not?

9. What were the words which Elisabeth Elliot shared with Steve that helped him understand the role of suffering in the life of a believer?

10. How has the Great Commission impacted your parents?

Worksheet 35.2

Practice Questions

1. How did Dr. Ralph Winter's speech change the way we looked at the state of unreached people?

2. What people groups are mentioned in Acts 1:8?

3. Who are a few of Steve's people groups in Lancaster County, Pennsylvania?

4. What is "people blindness"?

5. Where in Scripture are we commanded to preach the gospel and make disciples of all peoples?

6. Who was the first cross-cultural missionary?

7. What is the story of the book, *Through Gates of Splendor*?

Bible and Discussion Questions

8. Describe the contest on Mt. Carmel between Elijah, the prophet of God, and the priests of Baal.

9. What is the promise in Psalm 23 that God gives to each of His children?

10. What do your parents think of the idea of "people groups"?

Worksheet 35.3

Practice Questions

1. What does the word indigenous mean?

2. When missionaries have successfully planted a church in a new culture, what is their long-term strategy?

3. What verse shaped and influenced Steve when he had children? What were the two components of that passage?

4. Who is uniquely suited to train children to become citizens of heaven and earth? Why?

5. Why does Steve refer to parents as unique disciplers?

6. What is the long-term strategy of parents?

7. Why should missionaries and ministries emulate the natural order of parenting as they make disciples?

Bible and Discussion Questions

8. What do you think of the words of Joshua when he declares what he and his family have decided to do?

9. Why is Jesus able to identify with our suffering?

10. What are some organizations that are preaching the gospel around the world, that your parents admire and support?

Worksheet 35.4

Practice Questions

1. Why do you think Americans are particularly attracted to short-term mission trips?

2. Which short-term summer trips have proven successful and are needed?

3. What are some questionable fruits of a typical summer mission trip?

4. When Steve went on a summer trip, what were some of his reasons for going?

5. Who is Steve Saint? How is he connected to the five men who were killed on January 8, 1956?

6. Why does Steve Saint bring a unique perspective to the subject of missions?

7. What is the subject of *The Great Omission*? Do you think the author makes a valid point?

Bible and Discussion Questions

8. In the story of Elijah, how many other people in Israel had chosen to be faithful to God and not bow down to Baal?

9. What does it mean to be sanctified?

10. Are your parents and grandparents familiar with the story of the five men who were killed on January 8, 1956 while seeking to reach the Auca (Waorani)?

Worksheet 35.5

Practice Questions

1. What are some advantages that indigenous believers have over Western missionaries?

2. What are some advantages that Western missionaries have over indigenous believers?

3. What do indigenous believers need in order to fulfill the Great Commission?

4. What is ITEC? What do the initials stand for?

5. How are I-DENT, I-SEE, and I-MED helpful in preaching the gospel?

6. What does the following sentence mean? "People don't care how much you know until they know how much you care."

7. What attitude should Western missionaries cultivate when working with another culture?

Bible and Discussion Questions

8. What encourages Steve as he reads the book of Revelation?

9. How else can we be transformed to be like Jesus?

10. How has the Great Commission impacted the life of your grandparents?

Worksheet 36.1

Practice Questions

1. Why does Steve refer to people who have a disability as "affected by a disability?"

2. How did spending time at camp impact the way Steve viewed people affected with a disability?

3. How do we apply the command to love our neighbor as ourselves to special people with challenges?

4. Do most people affected by a disability choose to have a disability? Explain please.

5. If the percentages of special needs people are similar around the world, approximately how many people are affected by a disability in my county with 543,000 people?

6. How many of these special folks will have a significant disability?

7. What thoughts went through your mind when you read that this large group of people affected by disability are often the least evangelized?

Bible and Discussion Questions

8. When did God design the family? What was the makeup of the family created to be?

9. What does "fellowship of the Spirit" mean to Steve?

10. Have your parents heard of Joni or her ministry Joni and Friends? Joni is often characterized as the lady who paints with her teeth!

Worksheet 36.2

PRACTICE QUESTIONS

1. How well do churches respond to short-term needs like a broken leg?

2. Is having a disability a short-term or long-term need? Explain.

3. What did you think about the creative team effort to help the man in hospice care?

4. Why is being an usher so meaningful to Steve's son John?

5. How did Rick and Dave and the other men treat John that was so significant?

6. What is the special buddies program? How does it bless a family with a special-needs child?

7. What is another way someone who has a heart for special needs folks can serve?

Bible and Discussion Questions

8. Who preserved his family from a worldwide catastrophe? Approximately when did this occur?

9. What are two evidences of the ministry of the Spirit in the life of a believer?

10. Does your family have regular interaction with someone who is affected with a disability?

Worksheet 36.3

Practice Questions

1. What are some of the ways Steve and his wife have learned to treat John as they would like to be treated?

2. What are some benefits of work to John?

3. How have John's advocates helped him?

4. How has the inclusion of John and people who are hearing impaired been a win-win situation for Demme Learning?

5. What other organizations in the special-needs world partner with Demme Learning?

6. Do Psalm 139 and 1 Peter 4:10 apply to every man and woman affected by disability?

7. What gifts and contributions have special needs people like Joni, David, and John used to glorify God and edify His church?

Bible and Discussion Questions

8. What did Asaph exhort parents to teach their children in Psalm 78?

9. Who helps us assimilate and comprehend God's love for us? What scripture supports this truth?

10. What does your church do to reach out to "the poor, the crippled, the lame, and the blind"?

Worksheet 36.4

Practice Questions

1. My son John does not like snow. When he awakes and sees white stuff on our lawn he is upset, because he may not be able to go to work. Why do you think John loves going to work?

2. Why are employees at Demme Learning taking sign language classes?

3. How does John's job impact his caregivers, in this instance, my wife and myself?

4. Would you would rather stay home and receive a welfare check from the government, or go to work every day, be productive, and earn a paycheck?

5. Discuss the impact of inclusion of the EARS team onsite at our facility versus offsite assembly work at their location.

6. How are people with a disability the same as you?

7. How are people with a disability different than you?

Bible and Discussion Questions

8. What advice does Paul give to parents before instructing them about the Christian family?

9. Who has been responsible for inspiring men of God to write the Scriptures? How do we know?

10. Have your grandparents worked with or known well any people affected by a disability?

Worksheet 36.5

Practice Questions

1. If you had a disability, how would you like to be seen and treated?

2. Based on what you have learned, what are some ways that you can be an encouragement to someone with a physical challenge?

3. Can you think of others, besides people with a disability, that might also be one of "the least of these" that Jesus speaks about in Matthew 25?

4. Are disabilities a punishment? What scripture addresses this topic?

5. Why does Steve like "Redeemer" as a title for God?

6. What did you learn in this lesson that was new to you and changed your thinking about the disability community?

7. What was your chief takeaway from this lesson?

Bible and Discussion Questions

8. What are the qualifications for elders and deacons in church leadership?

9. Which verse expressing gratitude to the Spirit touches your heart the most?

10. Since this is your last discussion question, ask your parents/grandparents what their chief takeaway was from this course. Enjoy!